Assessments

Program Author
Gretchen Bernabei

 NATIONAL GEOGRAPHIC

 Hampton-Brown

Contents

Assessment to Inform Instruction

The *Good Writer's Kit* provides a comprehensive array of assessment tools that help you engage students in their own learning, evaluate student progress as you go, and benchmark overall writing performance.

Assessment Tool	Description	Diagnostic Evaluation	Progress Monitoring	Summative Evaluation
Benchmark Tests	Five parallel forms each focus on a type of writing commonly found on state exit exams—expository, persuasive, literary analysis, narrative, and reflective—and allow you to measure growth in writing proficiency across time. Each form includes a writing prompt as well as multiple-choice items to assess strategies for planning, revising, and editing compositions.	✓	✓	✓
Chapter Tests • **Pretest** • **Posttest**	Each chapter of the Good Writer's Guide has two parallel test forms. Use test form A before instruction to determine student needs. Use test form B after instruction to measure expected outcomes for the chapter.	✓		✓
Section Tests	A performance assessment for each section within a chapter provides ongoing information about students' growth in specific areas of writing proficiency, such as writing process strategies, writing traits, and effectiveness when writing for different purposes.		✓	
Affective Measures	Inventories and surveys encourage students to reflect on their own writing interests and attitudes toward writing.		✓	
Student Self- and Peer-Assessments	These forms help students reflect on and evaluate their own writing and the writing of others.		✓	
Process Assessments for Writing and Research • **Self-Evaluations** • **Checklists** • **Reflection Forms**	These tools help students reflect on and evaluate their own writing and research processes.		✓	
Good Writing Traits Rubric	Use this analytic rubric to score all types of student writing for the five Good Writing Traits: · Focus and Unity · Organization · Development of Ideas · Voice and Style · Written Conventions	✓	✓	✓

Benchmark Tests

Purpose and Description

The **Benchmark Tests** allow you to measure growth in writing proficiency across time. Each test form includes 12 multiple-choice items and one writing prompt. Each test form has three sections based on stages of the writing process: a planning task, a revising and editing task, and a writing task. These item types and tasks are commonly found on state exit exams. Each of the five benchmark tests focuses on a type of writing commonly found on state exit exams: expository, persuasive, literary analysis, narrative, and reflective.

Administering the Tests

Five test forms let you administer a benchmark test at the beginning, at the end, and up to three times during your program. Allow students a minimum of 50 minutes to take a benchmark test (20 minutes for the multiple-choice items and 30 minutes for the written composition). Some state exams allow 60 or more minutes to complete the written composition. Time permitting, we recommend that you allow the same amount of time as your state exam for the written composition. Photocopy a test for each student and provide separate sheets of paper for writing the composition.

Scoring the Tests

Use the Student Profile form at the end of each test to record test scores for each student. Score the multiple-choice items with the answer key on page 105. On the Student Profile, circle which items the student answered correctly. Score the written composition for each writing trait with the Good Writing Traits Rubric on page 11a–b. On the Student Profile, circle the student's rubric score for each trait. Add the number of multiple choice items correct to the rubric points earned to get trait scores. For an overall test score, total the trait points earned and divide by 32.

Using the Test Results

Benchmark tests report scores for each of the five writing traits. Focus instruction on those traits that require the most work. Chapter 2 of the Good Writer's Guide devotes a section to each of the five writing traits.

Benchmark Tests

Name _____
Date _____

Persuasive Writing

Directions: Ramiro created the opinion chart to organize ideas for his composition. Use his diagram to answer questions 1–3. Mark your answers as shown in the sample.

Ramiro's Opinion Chart

| Opinion: Soft drink machines should be removed from campus. |

Reason: Students are throwing away their money on over-priced soft drinks.	**Reason:** The soft drink machines often have problems.	**Reason:** Soft drinks are unhealthy.
Support: Most drinks in machines cost $1.25/bottle. You can buy a box for $.40/can in stores.	**Support:** Two days this week machines needed repairs.	**Support:** The sugar in soft drinks can cause tooth decay.

Sample
Based on Ramiro's chart, what type of composition is he planning to write?
Ⓐ expository
● persuasive
Ⓒ literary analysis
Ⓓ narrative

1. Which is the best title for Ramiro's composition?
Ⓐ Teens and Tooth Decay
Ⓑ An Unnecessary Expense
Ⓒ How to Fix a Soft-Drink Machine
Ⓓ Campus Is No Place for Soft Drinks

2. Which detail supports Ramiro's second reason, that soft drink machines often have problems?
Ⓕ Most high school students do not have jobs.
Ⓖ Tooth decay is caused by bacteria that feeds on sugar.
Ⓗ Repairs to the soft drink machines can be costly.
Ⓙ Too much sugar and caffeine can agitate students.

3. Based on the chart, how many paragraphs will the body of Ramiro's composition have?
Ⓐ 1
Ⓑ 3
Ⓒ 6
Ⓓ 9

GO ON

© Hampton-Brown   3a   Benchmark Tests

Persuasive Writing, continued

Name _____
Date _____

Directions: Tashara wrote the composition about lawsuits against fast-food chains. It is her first draft, and she wants you to help her improve it. Read her composition and answer questions 4–12.

The Blame Game: Lawsuits Against Fast-Food Chains

(1) Potter Stewart, a United States Supreme Court Justice, once said, "There's a big difference between what you have a right to do and what is right to do." (2) Our parents, teachers, and community have taught us to use good judgement and take responsibility for our actions. (3) Why, then, do some people file lawsuits that blame others for their personal decisions? (4) When people blame fast-food chains for their obesity, for example, I think these people are looking for an easy way out. (5) These people are blaming others for their own poor choices. (6) People should take responsibility for their actions. (7) They could start by learning about nutrition and exercise. (8) Most people should know that "fast food" usually means super-sized portions, and bad ingredients.

(9) Some people may argue that these lawsuits will force the fast-food industry to improve the quality of their food, but I think there are better ways to cause change. (10) For example, children and the general public need more education about the following fats, calories, carbohydrates, and chemical additives. (11) Educating people about nutrition would be most affective.

(12) In 2004, the US House of Representatives passed the Personal Responsibility in Food Consumption Act. (13) This act does not allow people to blame fast-food for their weight problems; they ban obesity lawsuits against fast-food chains.

(14) Those against fast-food chains, as frivolous lawsuits, show how some people do not take responsibility for their actions. (15) Fast-food chains are everywhere. (16) There is a big difference between having rights and doing right. (17) We are living in a free society, with the freedom to make our own personal choices. (18) Therefore, we should take responsibility for our choices—even when we make the wrong choices.

GO ON

© Hampton-Brown   3b   Benchmark Tests

Persuasive Writing, continued

Name _____

Date _____

4. Which is the correct way to spell the underlined word in sentence 2?

Ⓕ jugment

Ⓖ jugement

Ⓗ judgement

Ⓙ Leave as is.

5. Which transition should Tashara add to the beginning of sentence 6 to show a connection to the previous sentence?

Ⓐ Finally

Ⓑ Instead

Ⓒ Therefore

Ⓓ Consequently

6. Which is the most precise way to express meaning of the underlined word in sentence 8?

Ⓕ too many

Ⓖ unhealthy

Ⓗ super fast

Ⓙ disgusting

7. Which is the correct way to punctuate the underlined part of sentence 10?

Ⓐ the following fats

Ⓑ the following, fats

Ⓒ the following: fats

Ⓓ Leave as is.

8. Which is the best word to replace the underlined word in sentence 11?

Ⓕ affected

Ⓖ effective

Ⓗ defective

Ⓙ Leave as is.

9. Which are the correct words to replace the underlined part of sentence 13?

Ⓐ it bans

Ⓑ these ban

Ⓒ which bans

Ⓓ Leave as is.

10. Which sentence should Tashara add after sentence 13 to conclude paragraph 3?

Ⓕ I, for one, am very grateful that this legislation was passed by Congress.

Ⓖ Finally, people who try to get rich off fast-food businesses will be ignored.

Ⓗ Obesity is a serious health problem that our government needs to address.

Ⓙ Now what we need is additional legislation to protect our cigarette companies.

11. Which is the best way to write the underlined part of sentence 14?

Ⓐ Fast-food chains, with lawsuits that are frivolous,

Ⓑ Chains with fast food, and ones with frivolous lawsuits,

Ⓒ Frivolous lawsuits, such as those against fast-food chains,

Ⓓ Lawsuits against fast-food chains, which happen to be frivolous,

12. Which sentence is **not** related to the main idea of the last paragraph?

Ⓕ sentence 15

Ⓖ sentence 16

Ⓗ sentence 17

Ⓙ sentence 18

`GO ON` ➡

Persuasive Writing, continued

Name _____

Date _____

Directions: Read the writing prompt. Write your composition on separate sheets of paper. Use the checklist to make sure that you do your best work.

Writing Prompt

Your school board will be voting on whether to shorten the school day so that students can spend more time learning from real life.

Some people believe that students learn the most important things they need to know outside of the classroom. Others think that school teaches students everything they need to know.

Write a persuasive essay that will be read by the school board in which you convince them to vote with your position on this issue.

Checklist

☐ Write about all parts of the prompt.

☐ Present a clear central idea, and stay focused on it.

☐ Organize your composition from its introduction to its conclusion.

☐ Use transitions to connect your thoughts for the reader.

☐ Present meaningful ideas, and support them with specific information.

☐ Use appropriate words and a variety of sentence structures.

☐ Proofread and edit your writing for grammar, usage, mechanics, and spelling.

DONE!

TEACHER USE ONLY

Use the Good Writing Traits Rubric on pages 11a–b to score each trait. Transfer the score to the Student Profile form on page 4 in the Written Composition Rubric Scores column to factor them into the overall benchmark test score.

Focus and Unity	1	2	3	4
Organization	1	2	3	4
Idea Development	1	2	3	4
Voice and Style	1	2	3	4
Written Conventions	1	2	3	4

Use the Student Profile to record test scores for each student.

Benchmark Tests

Name _____

Date _____

Student Profile: Persuasive Writing

1) Use the answer key on page 103 to score the multiple-choice items. Circle the item number of each correct answer below. Multiple-choice items are worth one point each.

2) Use the Good Writing Traits Rubric on pages 11a–b to score the written composition. Circle the number of points earned for each writing trait below.

3) For each trait, add the number of correct multiple-choice items to the number of rubric points awarded. These are your student's writing trait scores. For an overall writing score, add the trait scores together. For an overall percentage, divide the total number of points earned by 32.

Writing Traits	Multiple-Choice Item Numbers (1 point each)	Written Composition Rubric Scores	Test Scores by Trait and Overall
Focus & Unity	1 2	1 2 3 4	____/6
Organization	3 5	1 2 3 4	____/6
Idea Development	10 12	1 2 3 4	____/6
Voice & Style	6 11	1 2 3 4	____/6
Written Conventions	4 7 8 9	1 2 3 4	____/8
TOTALS	12 points	20 points	**Overall Score** ____/32 = ____ %

Student Profiles report scores for each of five writing traits and an overall test score.

Chapter Tests

Purpose and Description

Each **Chapter Test** has two parallel forms, allowing for pre- and post-assessment. You may administer Form A before instruction to determine student needs and Form B after instruction to measure expected outcomes for the chapter. If you choose not to administer a pretest, you may use Form B as an alternative, post-instruction chapter test. Chapter test items reflect formats typically used on state exit exams—multiple-choice items and writing prompts.

Administering the Tests

Make a copy of the test for each student. If necessary, provide paper for the writing prompt. Students should not use their books during the test.

Scoring the Tests

Use the answer key on page 105 to score multiple-choice tests (Chapters 1, 2, and 5). Use the Good Writing Traits Rubric on page 11a to score the writing prompt tests (Chapters 3 and 4).

Using the Test Results

Use pretest results to determine which sections of the chapter to focus on. Use posttest and post-instruction results to measure improvement and expected outcomes for the chapter.

Opposite top of page:
Multiple-choice Tests
Forms A and B for Chapter 1

Opposite bottom of page:
Writing Prompt Tests
Forms A and B for Chapter 3

Assessment Guidelines, continued

Chapter 1 The Writing Process

Name _____
Date _____

Chapter Test: Form A

Directions: For question 1, order the stages of the writing process from 1 to 5 on the lines below.

1. Stages of the writing process:

   ___ Publishing
   ___ Editing/Proofreading
   ___ Drafting
   ___ Revising
   ___ Prewriting

Directions: For questions 2–10, mark your answer as shown in the sample.

Sample
During which stage of the writing process should a writer check for spelling errors?
Ⓐ drafting
Ⓑ prewriting
Ⓒ publishing
● editing/proofreading

2. During which stage of the writing process should a writer add graphics to a composition?
   Ⓐ revising
   Ⓑ drafting
   Ⓒ prewriting
   Ⓓ publishing

3. When editing and proofreading, a writer should
   Ⓕ narrow the focus of the topic.
   Ⓖ check for correct punctuation.
   Ⓗ determine the purpose for writing.
   Ⓙ consider changing the intended audience.

4. A writer should use transitional words and phrases to make a composition
   Ⓐ factual and truthful.
   Ⓑ exciting and colorful.
   Ⓒ clear and easy to read.
   Ⓓ convincing and persuasive.

5. When would a graphic organizer be most helpful to a writer?
   Ⓕ after making revisions
   Ⓖ before creating a draft
   Ⓗ when choosing an audience
   Ⓙ during the proofreading process

6. When revising, how should a writer share a composition?
   Ⓐ enter it to win a writing contest
   Ⓑ give it to other people for feedback
   Ⓒ send it to a magazine for publication
   Ⓓ read it to a crowd at an open-mike night

GO ON ▶

© Hampton-Brown   23a   Chapter 1: The Writing Process

Chapter 1 The Writing Process

Name _____
Date _____

Chapter Test: Form B

Directions: For question 1, order the stages of the writing process from 1 to 5 on the lines below.

1. Stages of the writing process:

   ___ Revising
   ___ Publishing
   ___ Editing/Proofreading
   ___ Prewriting
   ___ Drafting

Directions: For questions 2–10, mark your answer as shown in the sample.

Sample
During which stage of the writing process should a writer check for spelling errors?
Ⓐ drafting
Ⓑ prewriting
Ⓒ publishing
● editing/proofreading

2. During which stage of the writing process should a writer gather facts?
   Ⓐ revising
   Ⓑ drafting
   Ⓒ prewriting
   Ⓓ publishing

3. Which statement about drafting is true?
   Ⓕ You should write a draft all in one sitting.
   Ⓖ It is okay to skip prewriting and start drafting.
   Ⓗ As you write a draft, you have to stick to your plan.
   Ⓙ You should use a pencil and lined notebook paper for a draft.

4. When would a thesaurus be most helpful to a writer?
   Ⓐ drafting
   Ⓑ revising
   Ⓒ prewriting
   Ⓓ publishing

5. Which would a writer do during the publishing stage of the writing process?
   Ⓕ send a composition to a magazine
   Ⓖ add interesting details and examples
   Ⓗ use a graphic organizer to organize ideas
   Ⓙ replace general words with specific words

6. During which stage of the writing process might it be helpful to read a composition backward?
   Ⓐ drafting
   Ⓑ revising
   Ⓒ publishing
   Ⓓ editing/proofreading

GO ON ▶

© Hampton-Brown   24a   Chapter 1: The Writing Process

Chapter 3 Writing Clinic

Name _____
Date _____

Chapter Test: Form A

Directions: Choose one of the three prompts to write about. Write your composition on separate sheets of paper.

Prompt 1

Look at the picture.
Write a short story or narrative composition about the picture. You may want to ask yourself: Who is this person? What book was he reading before he put his head down? Where is he? Is anyone else there? Why is he so tired?

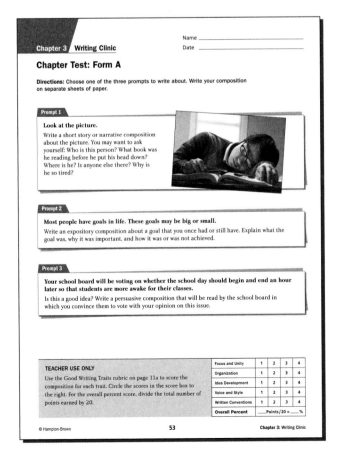

Prompt 2

Most people have goals in life. These goals may be big or small.
Write an expository composition about a goal that you once had or still have. Explain what the goal was, why it was important, and how it was or was not achieved.

Prompt 3

Your school board will be voting on whether the school day should begin and end an hour later so that students are more awake for their classes.
Is this a good idea? Write a persuasive composition that will be read by the school board in which you convince them to vote with your opinion on this issue.

TEACHER USE ONLY				
Use the *Good Writing Traits* rubric on page 11a to score the composition for each trait. Circle the scores in the score box to the right. For the overall percent score, divide the total number of points earned by 20.				

Focus and Unity	1	2	3	4
Organization	1	2	3	4
Idea Development	1	2	3	4
Voice and Style	1	2	3	4
Written Conventions	1	2	3	4
Overall Percent	____ Points / 20 = ____ %			

© Hampton-Brown   53   Chapter 3: Writing Clinic

Chapter 3 Writing Clinic

Name _____
Date _____

Chapter Test: Form B

Directions: Choose one of the three prompts to write about. Write your composition on separate sheets of paper.

Prompt 1

Look at the picture.
Write a short story or narrative composition about the picture. You may want to ask yourself: Who are these people? What does the music sound like? Where are they? Is anyone else there? Why is the girl playing a trumpet?

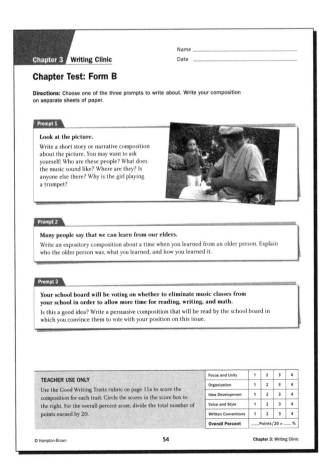

Prompt 2

Many people say that we can learn from our elders.
Write an expository composition about a time when you learned from an older person. Explain who the older person was, what you learned, and how you learned it.

Prompt 3

Your school board will be voting on whether to eliminate music classes from your school in order to allow more time for reading, writing, and math.
Is this a good idea? Write a persuasive composition that will be read by the school board in which you convince them to vote with your position on this issue.

TEACHER USE ONLY				
Use the *Good Writing Traits* rubric on page 11a to score the composition for each trait. Circle the scores in the score box to the right. For the overall percent score, divide the total number of points earned by 20.				

Focus and Unity	1	2	3	4
Organization	1	2	3	4
Idea Development	1	2	3	4
Voice and Style	1	2	3	4
Written Conventions	1	2	3	4
Overall Percent	____ Points / 20 = ____ %			

© Hampton-Brown   54   Chapter 3: Writing Clinic

Section Tests

Purpose and Description

The **Section Tests** are designed to provide ongoing information about students' growth in specific areas of writing proficiency. The tests may be based on writing and research processes (Chapters 1 and 5 Section Tests), revising and editing tasks (Chapter 3 Section Test), or writing tasks (Chapters 2 and 4 Section Tests).

Administering the Tests

Administer the test for each section after instruction. Make a copy of the test for each student. If necessary, provide paper for the revising task or writing prompt. Students should not use their books during the test.

Scoring the Tests

Score Section Tests with the rubrics provided. Sections in Chapters 1 and 5 are scored with process rubrics. Sections in Chapter 2 are scored with writing trait rubrics. Sections in Chapter 3 are scored with troubleshooting rubrics. Sections in Chapter 4 are scored with the Good Writing Traits Rubric on page 11a.

Using the Test Results

Use the test results to determine if the student understood the section instruction. If the student did not, analyze the performance assessment sample for more detailed, diagnostic information.

Opposite top of page:
Writing Prompt Section Tests
with checklists for students

Opposite bottom of page:
Revising Section Tests
with Solution reminders
for students

Assessment Guidelines, continued

Name _____
Date _____

Focus and Unity Test

Directions: Read the writing prompt. Write your composition on separate sheets of paper. Use the checklist to make sure that your writing is focused and unified.

Writing Prompt

New technology has changed the way people interact with each other.

Write a composition about some aspect of technology, and explain how it has changed the way people interact.

Checklist

- ❑ My composition presents a clear central idea.
- ❑ The main idea of each paragraph goes with the central idea of my composition.
- ❑ The main idea and details within each paragraph are related.
- ❑ The conclusion is about the central idea.

TEACHER USE ONLY
Use the Focus and Unity rubric and anchor samples on pages 27a–c to score the composition. Circle the score in the score box to the right.

Rubric Score	1	2	3	4
Percent Score	25%	50%	75%	100%

© Hampton-Brown
26
Chapter 2: Good Writing Traits

Name _____
Date _____

Written Conventions Test

Directions: Read the writing prompt. Write your composition on separate sheets of paper. Use the checklist to make sure that your composition is error free.

Writing Prompt

When people find themselves in new environments or situations, they often have to change or adapt.

Write a composition about a time when you or someone you know had to change or adapt to a new environment or situation.

Checklist

- ❑ My sentences are complete and correct.
- ❑ Any sentence fragments are used on purpose to achieve an effect.
- ❑ My punctuation, capitalization, and spelling are correct.

TEACHER USE ONLY
Use the Written Conventions rubric and anchor samples on pages 35a–c to score the composition. Circle the score in the score box to the right.

Rubric Score	1	2	3	4
Percent Score	25%	50%	75%	100%

© Hampton-Brown
34
Chapter 2: Good Writing Traits

Name _____
Date _____

Test: Writing Wanders

Directions: The writing wanders in the letter below. On a separate sheet of paper, rewrite the letter so that it is focused. Use the Solutions to help you revise.

Dear Principal Diaz:

I have heard that our school is thinking about buying a laptop for every student to use for school work. I think that is a great idea! It would be helpful for school in so many ways. We could take notes on a laptop. We could also IM friends in class. I hope they have a wireless Internet connection. I could even visit some friends on My Space. By the way, have you seen that You Tube video with the laughing hamster? Hilarious! I have a Mac at home.

Sincerely,
Josephine Ostas

Solutions:
- *Speak Your Truth:* Explain what you know in your heart.
- *Show Your Ideas in a Flow:* Use an idea organizer to map out your thoughts.

TEACHER USE ONLY
Use the Writing Wanders rubric on page 40 to score the revision. Circle the score in the score box to the right.

Rubric Score	1	2	3	4
Percent Score	25%	50%	75%	100%

© Hampton-Brown
39
Chapter 3: Writing Clinic

Name _____
Date _____

Test: Writing Is Too Vague

Directions: The writing is too vague in the paragraph below. On a separate sheet of paper, rewrite the paragraph so that it is clear and precise. Use the Solutions to help you revise.

My Shoes Lead an Active Life

Most shoes are boring, but not mine. My shoes like activity and excitement. They like to go places and play ball. My shoes dream of things like being in a big arena. My shoes are good because they do not like boring stuff.

Solutions:
- *Add Snapshots and Thoughtshots:* Describe in detail what you see and think.
- *Complete a Target Diagram:* Add layers and dimensions to your writing.
- *Use the Intensity Scale:* Use specific, precise words to say exactly what you mean.

VAGUE ━━━━━━━━━━━━━━━━━━━━▶ SHARP
general words   medium words   precise words

TEACHER USE ONLY
Use the Writing Is Too Vague rubric on page 46 to score the revision. Circle the score in the score box to the right.

Rubric Score	1	2	3	4
Percent Score	25%	50%	75%	100%

© Hampton-Brown
45
Chapter 3: Writing Clinic

Affective Measures

Purpose and Description

Personal interests and attitudes affect motivation. Motivation is an important factor in writing performance. The **Affective Measures** will help you and your students pursue their interests in and examine their attitudes toward writing.

Administration

Administer these inventories and surveys at your discretion. You may administer them at the beginning of the program to get a feel for students' interests and attitudes toward writing. You may administer them selectively, to engage students in the program. You may also administer them multiple times to compare any changes in interest and attitude over time.

Using the Results

Use individual results as a basis for discussion during teacher-student conferences. For a picture of overall class results, fill out the generic Class Tally Form (page 78) and tally individual student results. Whether looking at individual or class results, use the information to help engage students and get them writing.

Top of page:
Self-Assessment: Who Am I as a Writer?

Bottom of page:
Self-Assessment: How Do I Feel about Writing?

Tools | **Additional Assessments**

Name _____
Date _____

Self-Assessment: Who Am I as a Writer?

Directions: This survey will help you discover who you are as a writer. Answer parts A–D.

A. What interests me?

Directions: Put a ✔ next to all the topics that interest you. If you do not see your interests, add them to the list.

My Self
- hopes
- dreams
- strengths
- personality
- other: _____

My Country
- history
- government
- laws
- states/cities/towns
- other: _____

My Hobbies
- games/sports
- cars
- music/dance
- cooking
- other: _____

My Family
- parents
- brothers/sisters
- memories
- vacations
- other: _____

My World
- the environment
- travel/exploration
- history
- countries/cultures
- other: _____

My School
- teachers
- activities
- classmates
- classes
- other: _____

My Friends
- best friends
- disagreements
- helpful friends
- spending time together
- other: _____

My Beliefs
- values
- religion
- philosophy
- holidays
- other: _____

My Future
- job/college
- relationships
- apartment/house
- children
- other: _____

My Community
- the neighborhood
- neighborhood people
- doing things together
- things to improve
- other: _____

My Feelings
- fear
- excitement
- love
- wonder
- other: _____

Add to the List
- _____
- _____
- _____
- _____

Now list 3 topics that most interest you. Write why you are interested in them.

1. _____ Why? _____
2. _____ Why? _____
3. _____ Why? _____

© Hampton-Brown   79a   Tools: Additional Assessments

Tools | **Additional Assessments**

Name _____
Date _____

Self-Assessment: How Do I Feel about Writing?

Directions: Read the sentences about writing. Circle the numbers that show how much you agree or disagree with each sentence.

	Strongly Disagree	Disagree	Agree	Strongly Agree
❶ I like to write.	1	2	3	4
❷ I think I am a good writer.	1	2	3	4
❸ My teachers think that my writing is good.	1	2	3	4
❹ I write better about things that interest me.	1	2	3	4
❺ I like to share my writing with others.	1	2	3	4
❻ I like to help other people with their writing.	1	2	3	4
❼ Writing is easy for me.	1	2	3	4
❽ My writing is better than it used to be.	1	2	3	4
❾ I am trying to improve my writing.	1	2	3	4
❿ It is important to know how to write.	1	2	3	4

© Hampton-Brown   80   Tools: Additional Assessments

Self- and Peer-Assessments

The **Self- and Peer-Assessment** forms on pages 94 and 95 help students reflect on and evaluate their own writing and the writing of others. Students are prompted to comment on the strengths and weaknesses of written compositions. The Self- and Peer-Assessment forms can be used with all forms of writing.

The **Peer-Review** forms for Chapter 4 (pages 56-63) help students gather feedback on compositions written in the forms of writing addressed in Chapter 4 of the Good Writer's Guide. After students have completed a writing project for the chapter (e.g., writing a letter of problem solving), let students review each other's work using a Peer-Review form (e.g., Peer-Review: Letter of Problem Solving). After students have revised their compositions based on the feedback from their peers, score the compositions with the Good Writing Traits Rubric on page 11a. Enter student scores on the Class Record Form for the chapter.

Note to Teachers: The Good Writer's Guide writing projects for the sections of Chapter 4 serve as the section tests for the chapter. As stated above, score the compositions with the Good Writing Traits Rubric on page 11a.

Top of page:
Self-Assessment: Written Composition

Bottom of page:
Peer-Review: Letter of Problem Solving

Tools / **Additional Assessments**

Name _____
Date _____

Self-Assessment: Written Composition

Directions: Put a ✓ next to the form of writing that you used. Read your composition, and answer questions 1–4.

Writing Form

- ❑ reflective essay
- ❑ persuasive essay
- ❑ news article
- ❑ letter of problem solving
- ❑ literary critique
- ❑ poem in free verse
- ❑ short, short story
- ❑ résumé
- ❑ _____

1. What do you like best about your composition?
   _____
   _____
   _____

2. What did you do well?
   _____
   _____
   _____

3. What could you improve about your composition?
   _____
   _____
   _____

4. What will you remember to work on in your next composition?
   _____
   _____
   _____

© Hampton-Brown   94   Tools: Additional Assessments

Chapter 4 / **Writing Roles and Forms**

Reviewer _____
Writer _____
Date _____

Peer-Review: Letter of Problem Solving

Directions: Read your partner's letter. For questions 1–6, circle the number that matches your opinion of the letter.

Does the letter . . .	Needs Improvement	Well Done
❶ look professional and is it correctly formatted?	1	2
❷ clearly state the problem?	1	2
❸ contain facts and details about the problem?	1	2
❹ propose a clear solution?	1	2
❺ use a polite, yet firm tone?	1	2
❻ use standard written conventions?	1	2

Directions: Answer questions 7 and 8. If you need more room, use the back of the page.

7. What do you like best about your partner's letter? _____
   _____
   _____
   _____

8. How could your partner improve the letter? _____
   _____
   _____
   _____

© Hampton-Brown   57   Chapter 4: Writing Roles and Forms

Writing and Research Process Assessments

Any product, including a written composition, is the result of a process. That is why we have included a set of process assessments for each stage of the writing process and the research process.

1. Begin with the self-evaluations on page 81 and 97. For overall class results, tally individual student results in the Class Tally Form on page 78.

2. As students participate in the writing and research processes, allow them to monitor their progress with the checklists on pages 88–92 and 102–104.

3. After students have completed the writing and research processes, give them the Writing Process Reflection Form on page 82 and the Research Process Reflection Form on page 98. These will help your students refine their processes over time.

Tools / **Additional Assessments**

Name _____
Date _____

Self-Assessment: How Am I Doing with the Writing Process?

Directions: For many people, some stages of the writing process are easier to do than others. Read the list of things people do when they write. Circle the numbers that show how hard or how easy you think each stage is.

	Hard	Somewhat Hard	Somewhat Easy	Easy
❶ Deciding what I want to write about	1	2	3	4
❷ Organizing my thoughts for writing	1	2	3	4
❸ Thinking of enough things to say in my writing	1	2	3	4
❹ Getting feedback on my writing from others	1	2	3	4
❺ Changing my writing to make it better	1	2	3	4
❻ Correcting little mistakes in my writing	1	2	3	4
❼ Deciding when my writing is finished	1	2	3	4
❽ Sharing my writing with others	1	2	3	4

Directions: Answer questions 9 and 10. If you need more room, use the back of the page.

9. Which stage of the writing process do you think is the easiest? Explain why. _____
_____
_____

10. Which stage of the writing process do you think is the hardest? Explain why. _____
_____
_____

© Hampton-Brown   81   **Tools:** Additional Assessments

Tools / **Additional Assessments**

Name _____
Date _____

Self-Assessment: How Am I Doing with the Research Process?

Directions: For many people, some stages of the research process are easier to do than others. Read the list of things people do when they research. Circle the numbers that show how hard or how easy you think each stage is.

	Hard	Somewhat Hard	Somewhat Easy	Easy
❶ Planning your research	1	2	3	4
❷ Finding sources for information	1	2	3	4
❸ Choosing which sources to use	1	2	3	4
❹ Taking notes from your sources	1	2	3	4
❺ Making sense of your notes	1	2	3	4
❻ Turning your notes into an outline	1	2	3	4
❼ Adding your research to your report	1	2	3	4
❽ Citing the sources you used	1	2	3	4

Directions: Answer questions 9 and 10. If you need more room, use the back of the page.

9. Which stage of the research process do you think is the easiest? Explain why. _____
_____
_____

10. Which stage of the research process do you think is the hardest? Explain why. _____
_____
_____

© Hampton-Brown   97   **Tools:** Additional Assessments

Tools Additional Assessments

Name _____
Date _____

Prewriting Checklist

Directions: Use this checklist to help you prewrite your composition. If you do something else that helps you to get ready to write, check the last box and describe what you do.

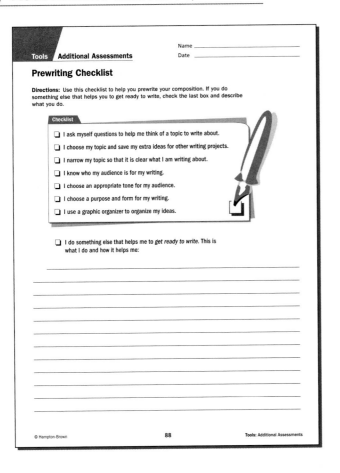

Checklist

- ☐ I ask myself questions to help me think of a topic to write about.
- ☐ I choose my topic and save my extra ideas for other writing projects.
- ☐ I narrow my topic so that it is clear what I am writing about.
- ☐ I know who my audience is for my writing.
- ☐ I choose an appropriate tone for my audience.
- ☐ I choose a purpose and form for my writing.
- ☐ I use a graphic organizer to organize my ideas.

☐ I do something else that helps me to *get ready to write*. This is what I do and how it helps me:

_____
_____
_____
_____
_____
_____
_____
_____
_____

© Hampton-Brown   88   **Tools:** Additional Assessments

Tools Additional Assessments

Name _____
Date _____

Digging Up the Facts Checklist

Directions: Use this checklist to help you dig up facts for your composition. If you do something else that helps you to gather information, check the last box and describe what you do.

Checklist

- ☐ I write research questions before searching for information.
- ☐ I narrow the focus of my research topic.
- ☐ I plan my search.
- ☐ I use different sources, such as books, the Internet, magazines, and interviews.
- ☐ I take careful notes.
- ☐ I avoid plagiarism.

☐ I do something else that helps me to gather information for my composition. This is what I do and how it helps me:

_____
_____
_____
_____
_____
_____
_____
_____
_____
_____
_____

© Hampton-Brown   102   **Tools:** Additional Assessments

Tools Additional Assessments

Name _____
Date _____

Writing Process Reflection Form

Directions: Reflect on the process you used to write your composition titled _____

Prewriting

1. What did you do that helped you brainstorm and plan your composition? _____

2. What will you do differently when you brainstorm and plan your next composition? _____

Drafting

3. What did you do that helped you draft your composition? _____

4. What will you do differently when you draft your next composition? _____

Revising

5. What did you do that helped you revise your composition? _____

6. What will you do differently when you revise your next composition? _____

Editing and Proofreading

7. What did you do that helped you edit your composition? _____

8. What will you do differently when you edit your next composition? _____

Publishing

9. What did you do that helped you publish your composition? _____

10. What will you do differently when you publish your next composition? _____

© Hampton-Brown   82   **Tools:** Additional Assessments

Tools Additional Assessments

Name _____
Date _____

Research Process Reflection Form

Directions: Reflect on the process you used to research your composition. Write the title of your composition here: _____

Gathering Information

1. What did you do that helped you gather information for your composition? _____

2. What will you do differently when you gather information for your next composition? _____

Organizing and Digesting Information

3. What did you do that helped you organize and digest information for your composition? _____

4. What will you do differently when you organize and digest information for your next composition? _____

Presenting Information

5. What did you do that helped you present information in your composition? _____

6. What will you do differently when you present information in your next composition? _____

© Hampton-Brown   98   **Tools:** Additional Assessments

Good Writing Traits Rubric

The **Good Writing Traits Rubric** combines the five individual writing trait rubrics of the Good Writer's Guide into a handy, analytic scoring tool. Assign 1 to 4 points for each of the five traits of good writing for any composition. Use it to evaluate compositions written to any of the numerous writing prompts presented in the Good Writer's Kit, or use it to evaluate compositions written to your own class assignments. For additional guidance, the rubric extension offers descriptions of how the five traits of good writing look in five common types of writing: expository, persuasive, literary analysis, narrative, and reflective.

Benchmark Tests

Rubric

Good Writing Traits

Score	Focus and Unity	Organization	Development of Ideas	Voice and Style	Written Conventions	Extension (see next page)
4	**Initial Focus:** Establishes a specific central idea about the topic. **Unity:** Individual paragraphs and the writing as a whole are focused on the controlling idea.	**Structure:** Effectively organizes the writing as a whole and each paragraph according to its purpose. **Coherence:** Leads the reader through ideas and support in an orderly way and with effective transitions.	**Content Quality:** Presents meaningful ideas in an interesting and engaging way. **Elaboration:** Thoroughly explains and supports ideas with relevant and specific information.	**Reader Engagement:** Fully engages the reader with an individual voice and style. Tone is consistent. **Words and Sentences:** Words are precise and effective. Sentences are varied and flow together effectively.	**Grammar and Usage:** Sentences are complete and correct. Fragments, if present, are used intentionally. **Mechanics and Spelling:** Demonstrates consistent control with few or no errors.	All or most of the features of the type of writing are present.
3	**Initial Focus:** Establishes a central idea about the topic. **Unity:** Individual paragraphs and the writing as a whole are mostly focused on the controlling idea.	**Structure:** Generally organizes the writing according to its purpose. **Coherence:** Leads the reader through most ideas and support in an orderly way and with adequate transitions.	**Content Quality:** Presents ideas in an interesting way. **Elaboration:** Adequately explains and supports most ideas with relevant information.	**Reader Engagement:** Mostly engages the reader with an individual voice and style. Tone is mostly consistent. **Words and Sentences:** Most words are precise and effective. Most sentences are varied and flow together.	**Grammar and Usage:** Most sentences are complete and correct. **Mechanics and Spelling:** Demonstrates control with minor errors.	Some of the features of the type of writing are present.
2	**Initial Focus:** Includes an overly general idea about the topic. **Unity:** Individual paragraphs and the writing as a whole are somewhat focused on the general idea.	**Structure:** Organizes the writing, but not according to its purpose. **Coherence:** Leads the reader through some ideas and support in an orderly way with a few transitions.	**Content Quality:** Presents ideas, but in an uninteresting way. **Elaboration:** Briefly explains and/or minimally supports some ideas.	**Reader Engagement:** Somewhat engages the reader, but the voice and style are not unique. **Words and Sentences:** Some words are effective. Some sentences are varied, but the flow could be smoother.	**Grammar and Usage:** Some sentences are complete and correct. **Mechanics and Spelling:** Demonstrates little control with frequent errors.	Few of the features of the type of writing are present.
1	**Initial Focus:** Addresses the topic too broadly. **Unity:** Individual paragraphs and the writing as a whole lack focus.	**Structure:** Lacks organization. **Coherence:** Ideas and support, if present, lack order and transitions.	**Content Quality:** Lacks clear ideas. **Elaboration:** Lacks explanation and support.	**Reader Engagement:** Does not engage the reader. **Words and Sentences:** Words are often vague. Sentences lack variety and do not flow together.	**Grammar and Usage:** Errors create a barrier to understanding. **Mechanics and Spelling:** Errors create a barrier to understanding.	Very few, if any, of the features of the type of writing are present.

© Hampton-Brown

11a

Benchmark Tests

Good Writing Traits Class Profile

The **Good Writing Traits Class Profile** form will help you plan instruction. It allows you to see at a glance the writing trait(s) that the majority of your students need to work on. Follow these steps to fill out the form:

1. At the top of the form, record the writing assignment and the date.

2. Write the student's initials in the cell that corresponds to the score he or she received in each trait. Each student's initials will appear in five cells—one for each trait.

3. After you have entered each student's initials, for each trait, find where most students are clustered and draw a dot in that cell. Connect the dots across the five traits to see in which traits your class is strongest and in which traits your class needs work.

Chapter 2 of the Good Writer's Guide devotes a section to each of the five writing traits. After a period of focused instruction, compare Class Profiles for subsequent writing assignments to see changes in class performance over time.

Good Writing Traits   **Class Profile**

Assignment _____ Date _____ Period _____

Directions: Use the **Good Writing Traits Rubric** on page 11a to score students' written compositions. Then plot the scores on the Rubric below by writing each student's initials in the appropriate cell. Identify the trait(s) with which the most students need practice. Use Chapter 2 of the Good Writer's Guide to focus instruction on a writing trait.

Scale	Focus & Unity	Organization	Development of Ideas	Voice & Style	Written Conventions
4					
3					
2					
1					

© Hampton-Brown

77

Tools: Additional Assessments

Tracking and Record Forms

The Good Writing Kit is designed to give you the freedom to move from one section to another in order to meet the needs of your students. The **Tracking Form for Tests Assigned** (page 76) will help you keep track of which chapter, section, or benchmark tests you administered to whom and when. Follow these steps to complete the form:

1. Write the names of your students along the top row so that each has an assigned column.

2. After administering a test to a student, find the row of the test administered and the student's column.

3. Write the administration date in the appropriate cell.

A **Class Record Form** has been provided for each chapter. Use it to record each student's section and chapter test scores. Follow these steps to complete the form:

1. Write the names of your students down the left column so that each has an assigned row.

2. After scoring a student's test, find the student's row and the column of the test.

3. Write the score(s) in the appropriate cell.

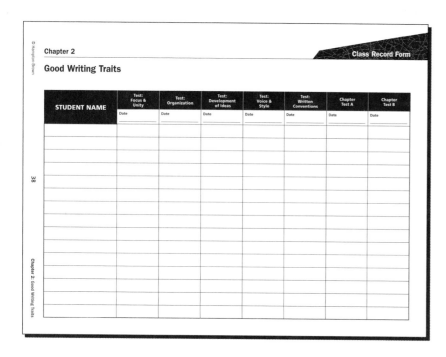

Benchmark Tests

Name _____

Date _____

Expository Writing

Directions: Angelina created the main idea and detail diagram to organize ideas for her composition. Use her diagram to answer questions 1–3. Mark your answers as shown in the sample.

Angelina's Main Idea and Detail Diagram

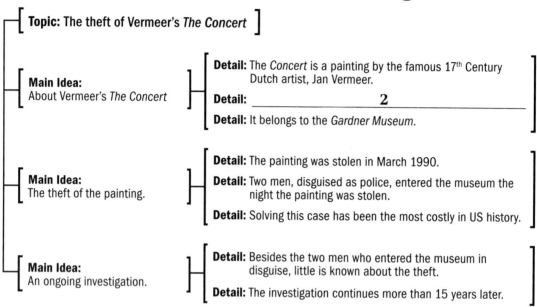

Topic: The theft of Vermeer's *The Concert*

Main Idea: About Vermeer's *The Concert*

Detail: The *Concert* is a painting by the famous 17th Century Dutch artist, Jan Vermeer.

Detail: _____ 2 _____

Detail: It belongs to the *Gardner Museum*.

Main Idea: The theft of the painting.

Detail: The painting was stolen in March 1990.

Detail: Two men, disguised as police, entered the museum the night the painting was stolen.

Detail: Solving this case has been the most costly in US history.

Main Idea: An ongoing investigation.

Detail: Besides the two men who entered the museum in disguise, little is known about the theft.

Detail: The investigation continues more than 15 years later.

Sample

Based on Angelina's diagram, what type of composition is she planning to write?

Ⓐ expository

Ⓑ persuasive

Ⓒ literary analysis

Ⓓ narrative

---

1. Which is the best title for Angelina's composition?

Ⓐ All About Vermeer

Ⓑ Art Theft: Serious Business

Ⓒ Vermeer and His Famous Painting that was Stolen

Ⓓ An Ongoing Investigation: The Case of *The Concert*

---

2. Which detail goes in the blank line in Angelina's diagram?

Ⓕ *The Concert* was painted around 1665.

Ⓖ Vermeer is known for 35 famous paintings.

Ⓗ Authorities do not know who stole *The Concert*.

Ⓙ Many theories about the theft of *The Concert* exist.

---

3. Which detail is in the wrong place in Angelina's diagram?

Ⓐ The painting was stolen in March 1990.

Ⓑ It belongs to the *Gardner Museum*.

Ⓒ The investigation continues more than 15 years later.

Ⓓ Solving this case has been the most costly in US history.

Expository Writing, continued

Directions: Peter wrote the composition about Cesar Chavez's work. It is his first draft, and he wants you to help him improve it. Read his composition and answer questions 4–12.

Labor for Justice: Cesar Chavez's Work

(1) César Chavez devoted his life to helping people.   (2) He was an American farm worker, labor leader, and activist who helped create fair laws for farm workers in the United States.

(3) César Chavez was born in Arizona in 1927.   (4) When he <u>was 14 Chavez</u> became a farm worker to help support his family.   (5) As a farm worker, Chavez <u>begins</u> to see the injustices farm workers faced.   (6) He saw farm laborers living in <u>awful</u> places without running water, electricity, or bathrooms. (7) Laborers were forced to live under unsanitary conditions because they were paid meager wages.   (8) The workers often had to work with dangerous chemicals without proper protections, such as gloves or masks.   (9) Working with these chemicals without protections <u>effected</u> the laborers' health and put their lives at risk.

(10) After seeing how unfairly farm workers were treated, Chavez made up his mind to make a difference.   (11) In 1952, he began working with civil rights groups.   (12) Together, Chavez and civil rights groups worked to educate laborers about the importance of voting.   (13) Chavez gave many public speeches about farm workers' rights.   (14) Chavez then co-founded the United Farm Workers Association (UFWA), <u>a place</u> that helped educate the community about the workers' unfair conditions.   (15) The UFWA also holds peaceful protests on behalf of laborers working under poor conditions.

(16) César Chavez dedicated his life to helping people attain their rights and educating the public about the working conditions of many farm workers.   (17) In 1994, after Chavez's death, President Clinton honored him with the U.S. Medal of Freedom.   (18) Presidents also can give this medal to people who are still alive.   (19) This medal acknowledges Chavez's lifelong contribution to helping others.

GO ON

Name _____

Date _____

4. Which is the correct way to punctuate the underlined part of sentence 4?

   Ⓕ was 14, Chavez

   Ⓖ was 14; Chavez

   Ⓗ was 14: Chavez

   Ⓙ Leave as is.

5. Which is the correct word to replace the underlined word in sentence 5?

   Ⓐ begin

   Ⓑ began

   Ⓒ begun

   Ⓓ Leave as is.

6. Which is the correct way to spell the underlined word in sentence 6?

   Ⓕ awfull

   Ⓖ aweful

   Ⓗ awefull

   Ⓙ Leave as is.

7. Which transition should Peter add to the beginning of sentence 8 to show a connection to the previous sentence?

   Ⓐ However

   Ⓑ Therefore

   Ⓒ In addition

   Ⓓ Even though

8. Which is the best word to replace the underlined word in sentence 9?

   Ⓕ defected

   Ⓖ affected

   Ⓗ infected

   Ⓙ Leave as is.

9. Which is the best way to combine sentences 11 and 12?

   Ⓐ He and civil rights groups, beginning in 1952, and working to educate laborers about the importance of voting.

   Ⓑ He began working with civil rights groups to educate laborers about the importance of voting; they began in 1952.

   Ⓒ In 1952, he began working with civil rights groups to educate laborers about the importance of voting.

   Ⓓ In 1952, he began working with civil rights groups, together they worked to educate laborers about the importance of voting.

10. Which sentence should Peter add after sentence 13 to support the ideas in paragraph 3?

    Ⓕ Chavez was a good public speaker.

    Ⓖ Farm workers' rights then became legal.

    Ⓗ Civil rights groups talked to the laborers too.

    Ⓙ He urged workers to ask for better conditions.

11. Which is the most precise way to express the meaning of the underlined word in sentence 14?

    Ⓐ a bunch

    Ⓑ a government

    Ⓒ an area

    Ⓓ an organization

12. Which sentence is **not** related to the main idea of the last paragraph?

    Ⓕ sentence 16

    Ⓖ sentence 17

    Ⓗ sentence 18

    Ⓙ sentence 19

GO ON ➡

Name _____

Date _____

Directions: Read the writing prompt. Write your composition on separate sheets of paper. Use the checklist to make sure that you do your best work.

Writing Prompt

We all have an activity that we enjoy doing. It could be an activity that we do once in a while, like riding on a roller coaster. It could be an activity that we do all the time, like jogging every morning before school. It could even be an activity that is barely active, like sleeping in on Saturday mornings.

Write an essay about an activity that you enjoy doing. Be sure to describe the activity and explain why you enjoy doing it.

Checklist

- ❏ Write about all parts of the prompt.
- ❏ Present a clear central idea, and stay focused on it.
- ❏ Organize your composition from its introduction to its conclusion.
- ❏ Use transitions to connect your thoughts for the reader.
- ❏ Present meaningful ideas, and support them with specific information.
- ❏ Use appropriate words and a variety of sentence structures.
- ❏ Proofread and edit your writing for grammar, usage, mechanics, and spelling.

DONE!

TEACHER USE ONLY

Use the Good Writing Traits Rubric on pages 11a–b to score each trait. Transfer the score to the Student Profile form on page 2 in the Written Composition Rubric Scores column to factor them into the overall benchmark test score.

Focus and Unity	1	2	3	4
Organization	1	2	3	4
Idea Development	1	2	3	4
Voice and Style	1	2	3	4
Written Conventions	1	2	3	4

Name _____

Date _____

Student Profile: Expository Writing

1) Use the answer key on page 103 to score the multiple-choice items. Circle the item number of each correct answer below. Multiple-choice items are worth one point each.

2) Use the Good Writing Traits Rubric on pages 11a–b to score the written composition. Circle the number of points earned for each writing trait below.

3) For each trait, add the number of correct multiple-choice items to the number of rubric points awarded. These are your student's writing trait scores. For an overall writing score, add the trait scores together. For an overall percentage, divide the total number of points earned by 32.

Writing Traits	Multiple-Choice Item Numbers (1 point each)	Written Composition Rubric Scores	Test Scores by Trait and Overall
Focus & Unity	1 2	1 2 3 4	____/6
Organization	3 7	1 2 3 4	____/6
Idea Development	10 12	1 2 3 4	____/6
Voice & Style	9 11	1 2 3 4	____/6
Written Conventions	4 5 6 8	1 2 3 4	____/8
TOTALS	12 points	20 points	Overall Score ____/32 = ____%

Name _____

Date _____

Persuasive Writing

Directions: Ramiro created the opinion chart to organize ideas for his composition. Use his diagram to answer questions 1–3. Mark your answers as shown in the sample.

Ramiro's Opinion Chart

Opinion: Soft drink machines should be removed from campus.

Reason: Students are throwing away their money on over-priced soft drinks.	**Reason:** The soft drink machines often have problems.	**Reason:** Soft drinks are unhealthy.
Support: Most drinks in machines cost $1.25/bottle. You can buy a box for $.40/can in stores.	**Support:** Two days this week machines needed repairs.	**Support:** The sugar in soft drinks can cause tooth decay.

Sample

Based on Ramiro's chart, what type of composition is he planning to write?

Ⓐ expository

Ⓑ persuasive

Ⓒ literary analysis

Ⓓ narrative

1. Which is the best title for Ramiro's composition?

Ⓐ Teens and Tooth Decay

Ⓑ An Unnecessary Expense

Ⓒ How to Fix a Soft-Drink Machine

Ⓓ Campus Is No Place for Soft Drinks

2. Which detail supports Ramiro's second reason, that soft drink machines often have problems?

Ⓕ Most high school students do not have jobs.

Ⓖ Tooth decay is caused by bacteria that feeds on sugar.

Ⓗ Repairs to the soft drink machines can be costly.

Ⓙ Too much sugar and caffeine can agitate students.

3. Based on the chart, how many paragraphs will the body of Ramiro's composition have?

Ⓐ 1

Ⓑ 3

Ⓒ 6

Ⓓ 9

GO ON →

Name _____

Date _____

Directions: Tashara wrote the composition about lawsuits against fast-food chains. It is her first draft, and she wants you to help her improve it. Read her composition and answer questions 4–12.

The Blame Game: Lawsuits Against Fast-Food Chains

(1) Potter Stewart, a United States Supreme Court Justice, once said, "There's a big difference between what you have a right to do and what is right to do." (2) Our parents, teachers, and community have taught us to use good judgement and take responsibility for our actions. (3) Why, then, do some people file lawsuits that blame others for their personal decisions? (4) When people blame fast-food chains for their obesity, for example, I think these people are looking for an easy way out. (5) These people are blaming others for their own poor choices. (6) People should take responsibility for their actions. (7) They could start by learning about nutrition and exercise. (8) Most people should know that "fast food" usually means super-sized portions, and bad ingredients.

(9) Some people may argue that these lawsuits will force the fast-food industry to improve the quality of their food, but I think there are better ways to cause change. (10) For example, children and the general public need more education about the following fats, calories, carbohydrates, and chemical additives. (11) Educating people about nutrition would be most affective.

(12) In 2004, the US House of Representatives passed the Personal Responsibility in Food Consumption Act. (13) This act does not allow people to blame fast-food for their weight problems; they ban obesity lawsuits against fast-food chains.

(14) Those against fast-food chains, as frivolous lawsuits, show how some people do not take responsibility for their actions. (15) Fast-food chains are everywhere. (16) There is a big difference between having rights and doing right. (17) We are living in a free society, with the freedom to make our own personal choices. (18) Therefore, we should take responsibility for our choices—even when we make the wrong choices.

GO ON

4. Which is the correct way to spell the underlined word in sentence 2?

 (F) jugment

 (G) jugement

 (H) jugdement

 (J) Leave as is.

5. Which transition should Tashara add to the beginning of sentence 6 to show a connection to the previous sentence?

 (A) Finally

 (B) Instead

 (C) Therefore

 (D) Consequently

6. Which is the most precise way to express the meaning of the underlined word in sentence 8?

 (F) too many

 (G) unhealthy

 (H) super fast

 (J) disgusting

7. Which is the correct way to punctuate the underlined part of sentence 10?

 (A) the following fats

 (B) the following, fats

 (C) the following: fats

 (D) Leave as is.

8. Which is the best word to replace the underlined word in sentence 11?

 (F) affected

 (G) effective

 (H) defective

 (J) Leave as is.

9. Which are the correct words to replace the underlined part of sentence 13?

 (A) it bans

 (B) these ban

 (C) which bans

 (D) Leave as is.

10. Which sentence should Tashara add after sentence 13 to conclude paragraph 3?

 (F) I, for one, am very grateful that this legislation was passed by Congress.

 (G) Finally, people who try to get rich off fast-food businesses will be ignored.

 (H) Obesity is a serious health problem that our government needs to address.

 (J) Now what we need is additional legislation to protect our cigarette companies.

11. Which is the best way to write the underlined part of sentence 14?

 (A) Fast-food chains, with lawsuits that are frivolous,

 (B) Chains with fast food, and ones with frivolous lawsuits,

 (C) Frivolous lawsuits, such as those against fast-food chains,

 (D) Lawsuits against fast-food chains, which happen to be frivolous,

12. Which sentence is **not** related to the main idea of the last paragraph?

 (F) sentence 15

 (G) sentence 16

 (H) sentence 17

 (J) sentence 18

GO ON ➤

Name _____

Date _____

Directions: Read the writing prompt. Write your composition on separate sheets of paper. Use the checklist to make sure that you do your best work.

Writing Prompt

Your school board will be voting on whether to shorten the school day so that students can spend more time learning from real life.

Some people believe that students learn the most important things they need to know outside of the classroom. Others think that school teaches students everything they need to know.

Write a persuasive essay that will be read by the school board in which you convince them to vote with your position on this issue.

Checklist

❏ Write about all parts of the prompt.

❏ Present a clear central idea, and stay focused on it.

❏ Organize your composition from its introduction to its conclusion.

❏ Use transitions to connect your thoughts for the reader.

❏ Present meaningful ideas, and support them with specific information.

❏ Use appropriate words and a variety of sentence structures.

❏ Proofread and edit your writing for grammar, usage, mechanics, and spelling.

DONE!

TEACHER USE ONLY

Use the Good Writing Traits Rubric on pages 11a–b to score each trait. Transfer the score to the Student Profile form on page 4 in the Written Composition Rubric Scores column to factor them into the overall benchmark test score.

Focus and Unity	1	2	3	4
Organization	1	2	3	4
Idea Development	1	2	3	4
Voice and Style	1	2	3	4
Written Conventions	1	2	3	4

Name _____

Date _____

Student Profile: Persuasive Writing

1) Use the answer key on page 103 to score the multiple-choice items. Circle the item number of each correct answer below. Multiple-choice items are worth one point each.

2) Use the Good Writing Traits Rubric on pages 11a–b to score the written composition. Circle the number of points earned for each writing trait below.

3) For each trait, add the number of correct multiple-choice items to the number of rubric points awarded. These are your student's writing trait scores. For an overall writing score, add the trait scores together. For an overall percentage, divide the total number of points earned by 32.

Writing Traits	Multiple-Choice Item Numbers (1 point each)	Written Composition Rubric Scores	Test Scores by Trait and Overall
Focus & Unity	1 2	1 2 3 4	_____/6
Organization	3 5	1 2 3 4	_____/6
Idea Development	10 12	1 2 3 4	_____/6
Voice & Style	6 11	1 2 3 4	_____/6
Written Conventions	4 7 8 9	1 2 3 4	_____/8
TOTALS	12 points	20 points	Overall Score _____/32 = _____%

Name _____

Date _____

Literary Analysis

Directions: Lisa created the web to organize ideas for her composition. Use her web to answer questions 1–3. Mark your answers as shown in the sample.

Lisa's Web

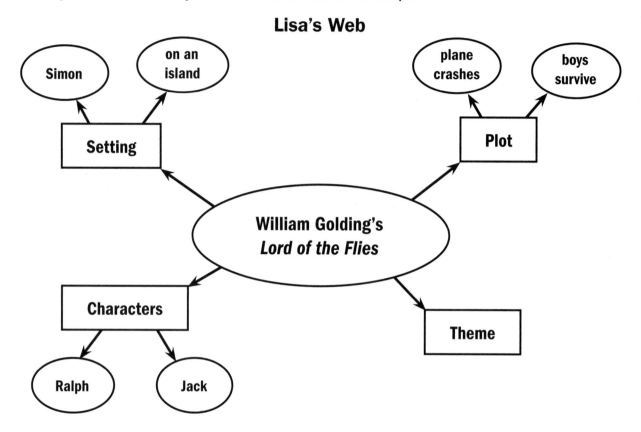

Sample

Based on Lisa's web, what type of composition is she planning to write?

Ⓐ expository

Ⓑ persuasive

Ⓒ literary analysis

Ⓓ narrative

1. Which is the best title for Lisa's composition?

    Ⓐ *Lord of the Flies*: Who's Who

    Ⓑ The Theme of *Lord of the Flies*

    Ⓒ *Lord of the Flies*: Plot and Setting

    Ⓓ The Literary Elements of *Lord of the Flies*

2. Under which heading should Lisa add the detail that war breaks out among the boys?

    Ⓕ Plot

    Ⓖ Theme

    Ⓗ Setting

    Ⓙ Characters

3. Which detail is in the wrong place in Lisa's web?

    Ⓐ Ralph

    Ⓑ Simon

    Ⓒ on an island

    Ⓓ plane crashes

GO ON ➡

Directions: Akeem wrote the composition about "The Red Wheelbarrow." It is his first draft, and he wants you to help him improve it. Read his composition and answer questions 4–12.

Imagery and Symbolism in "The Red Wheelbarrow"

(1) In his poem "The Red Wheelbarrow," William Carlos Williams uses the literary <u>devises</u> of imagery and symbolism.   (2) This short poem contains images of a simple, rural setting.   (3) This poem's simple setting symbolizes the importance of observing life's small details to appreciate life's greater meaning.

(4) The opening, "so much depends upon a red wheelbarrow," tells the reader that the wheelbarrow is important to the life of the scene.   (5) Most people would consider a wheelbarrow an ordinary, functional <u>tool; however; Williams</u> portrays the wheelbarrow as a beautiful and significant symbol.
(6) With its warm, red color, Williams shows the wheelbarrow as a robust tool.
(7) Its strength represents helpfulness to human work.   (8) Farmers use wheelbarrows to haul a variety of materials.   (9) "Glazed with rain water," the wheelbarrow gleams with nature's purest substance.   (10) Shown together, both rain and the wheelbarrow are viewed as dependable and much needed <u>stuff</u> for survival.   (11) As the wheelbarrow sits "beside the white chickens," <u>their</u> is a hint of activity to an otherwise static scene.   (12) The "white chickens" contrast with the "red wheelbarrow" not only with their activity but <u>additionally with their color as well also.</u>   (13) Together they produce a vibrant setting.

(14) "The Red Wheelbarrow" uses imagery and symbolism of simple objects and animals to show the world's greatness.   (15) To understand the bigger picture of this rural scene, <u>the reader must focus on the details of the rain, the wheelbarrow, and the chickens.</u>   (16) The reader then understands that to make sense of the bigger picture of the world, "so much depends upon" being an active observer of the details in life.

GO ON

4. Which is the correct way to spell the underlined word in sentence 1?

   Ⓕ divices

   Ⓖ divises

   Ⓗ devices

   Ⓙ Leave as is.

5. Which transition should Akeem add to the beginning of sentence 3 to show a connection to the previous sentence?

   Ⓐ Firstly

   Ⓑ Therefore

   Ⓒ Furthermore

   Ⓓ Instead

6. Which is the correct way to punctuate the underlined part of sentence 5?

   Ⓕ tool; however, Williams

   Ⓖ tool, however; Williams

   Ⓗ tool, however, Williams

   Ⓙ Leave as is.

7. Which sentence is **not** related to the main idea of paragraph 2?

   Ⓐ sentence 6

   Ⓑ sentence 7

   Ⓒ sentence 8

   Ⓓ sentence 9

8. Which is the most precise way to express the meaning of the underlined word in sentence 10?

   Ⓕ things

   Ⓖ weather

   Ⓗ creatures

   Ⓙ resources

9. Which is the correct word to replace the underlined word in sentence 11?

   Ⓐ here

   Ⓑ there

   Ⓒ they're

   Ⓓ Leave as is.

10. Which is the best way to write the underlined part of sentence 12?

    Ⓕ also with their color

    Ⓖ also with their color as well

    Ⓗ additionally with their color as well

    Ⓙ Leave as is.

11. Which is the correct way to write the underlined part of sentence 15?

    Ⓐ the rain, the wheelbarrow, and the chickens require the reader's focus

    Ⓑ the details of the rain, the wheelbarrow, and the chickens require reader focus

    Ⓒ the focus of the reader on the rain, the wheelbarrow, and the chickens require reader focus

    Ⓓ Leave as is.

12. Which sentence should Akeem add after sentence 16 to conclude the last paragraph?

    Ⓕ In this way, readers come to understand Williams' poem.

    Ⓖ The poem, "The Red Wheelbarrow," while short, communicates a great deal.

    Ⓗ The poem, "The Red Wheelbarrow," expresses Williams' picture of his world.

    Ⓙ In this way, readers of the poem come to understand the world in which they live.

GO ON

Name _____

Date _____

Directions: Read the writing prompt. Write your composition on separate sheets of paper. Use the checklist to make sure that you do your best work.

Writing Prompt

Literature can teach us important lessons about life. Think of a lesson you learned from reading a work of literature. It may be something you read in or out of school.

Write an essay in which you identify the work of literature and explain how it taught you a lesson about life.

Checklist

- ❑ Write about all parts of the prompt.
- ❑ Present a clear central idea, and stay focused on it.
- ❑ Organize your composition from its introduction to its conclusion.
- ❑ Use transitions to connect your thoughts for the reader.
- ❑ Present meaningful ideas, and support them with specific information.
- ❑ Use appropriate words and a variety of sentence structures.
- ❑ Proofread and edit your writing for grammar, usage, mechanics, and spelling.

DONE!

TEACHER USE ONLY

Use the Good Writing Traits Rubric on pages 11a–b to score each trait. Transfer the score to the Student Profile form on page 6 in the Written Composition Rubric Scores column to factor them into the overall benchmark test score.

Focus and Unity	1	2	3	4
Organization	1	2	3	4
Idea Development	1	2	3	4
Voice and Style	1	2	3	4
Written Conventions	1	2	3	4

Name _____

Date _____

Student Profile: Literary Writing

1) Use the answer key on page 103 to score the multiple-choice items. Circle the item number of each correct answer below. Multiple-choice items are worth one point each.

2) Use the Good Writing Traits Rubric on pages 11a–b to score the written composition. Circle the number of points earned for each writing trait below.

3) For each trait, add the number of correct multiple-choice items to the number of rubric points awarded. These are your student's writing trait scores. For an overall writing score, add the trait scores together. For an overall percentage, divide the total number of points earned by 32.

Writing Traits	Multiple-Choice Item Numbers (1 point each)	Written Composition Rubric Scores	Test Scores by Trait and Overall
Focus & Unity	1 2	1 2 3 4	_____/6
Organization	3 5	1 2 3 4	_____/6
Idea Development	7 12	1 2 3 4	_____/6
Voice & Style	8 10	1 2 3 4	_____/6
Written Conventions	4 6 9 11	1 2 3 4	_____/8
TOTALS	12 points	20 points	Overall Score _____/32 = _____%

Name _____

Date _____

Narrative Writing

Directions: Kikumi created the sequence chain to organize ideas for her composition. Use her sequence chain to answer questions 1–3. Mark your answers as shown in the sample.

Kikumi's Sequence Chain

Beginning: My dad and I leave the house at 10 a.m. Mom and my brother stay at home.

Event 1: We go downtown for our favorite breakfast burrito with warm tortillas.

Event 2: We go to the music store and listen to sample songs on headphones. Dad buys me a new music CD. The waitress always smiles at us.

Event 3: We drive across town to the movie theatre so we can see the latest horror movie. I get scared, but my dad just laughs.

Ending: We return home and tell mom and my brother all about our day.

Sample

Based on Kikumi's sequence chain, what type of composition is she planning to write?

Ⓐ persuasive

Ⓑ literary analysis

● narrative

Ⓓ reflective

---

1. Which is the best title for Kikumi's composition?

Ⓐ The Scary Movie

Ⓑ Family Weekend

Ⓒ My Brother and Mom

Ⓓ A Great Day with Dad

2. Under which heading should Kikumi add the name of her new music CD?

Ⓕ Beginning

Ⓖ Event 1

Ⓗ Event 2

Ⓙ Event 3

3. Which detail is in the wrong place in Kikumi's sequence chain?

Ⓐ Dad buys me a new music CD.

Ⓑ The waitress always smiles at us.

Ⓒ Mom and my brother stay at home.

Ⓓ I get scared, but my dad just laughs.

GO ON ➡

Directions: Manuel wrote the composition about Jane Goodall's work with chimpanzees. It is his first draft, and he wants you to help him improve it. Read his composition and answer questions 4–12.

Jane Goodall: Making A Difference

(1) Dr. Jane Goodall spent much of her adult life in the forests of Africa, where she discovered amazing facts about chimpanzees. (2) Her discoveries marked a new understanding of nonhuman primates. (3) Her findings also marked the importance of preserving the natural habitats of all animals.

(4) Jane Goodall was born in London, England on April 3, 1934. (5) When she was eight years old, her parents divorced. (6) She moved to Bournemouth, England, with her mother.

(7) Goodall became interested in animals at a <u>young age she</u> dreamed of studying them. (8) After she finished school, Goodall worked as a secretary for Louis Leakey, a noted anthropologist. (9) Goodall traveled to Kenya with Leakey. (10) Then, in the summer of 1960, Goodall fulfilled her childhood dream of <u>being with</u> animals. (11) She set up camp on the shore of Gombe Stream National Park in Tanzania, Africa. (12) This park was established to protect animals and allow people to see them in the wild. (13) Her plan was to carefully observe chimpanzees in their natural habitat.

(14) Goodall's twenty-five years with the chimpanzees was a ground-breaking study. (15) Goodall discovered that chimpanzees are capable of having lasting relationships, using tools, and adopting orphaned babies. (16) She even <u>witnesses</u> chimpanzees declaring a four-year war! (17) After this extensive research, Goodall was inspired to extend her work into other areas of the environment.

(18) In 1977, Goodall founded the Jane Goodall Institute for Wildlife Research, Education, and Conservation. (19) The institute's initial mission was to provide ongoing support to the world's chimpanzee population. (20) The institute's mission is to "advance the power of individuals to take informed and <u>compassionate</u> action to improve the environment for all living things." (21) Jane Goodall now spends her time heading the institute and encouraging young people to make a difference in <u>they're</u> world.

GO ON ➤

Name _____

Date _____

4. Which is the best way to combine sentences 5 and 6?

   Ⓕ Her parents divorcing when she was eight years old and moving to Bournemouth, England, with her mother.

   Ⓖ When she was eight years old, her parents divorced, she moved to Bournemouth, England, with her mother.

   Ⓗ When she was eight years old, her parents divorced, and she moved to Bournemouth, England, with her mother.

   Ⓙ She moved to Bournemouth, England, with her mother when she was eight years old and after her parents divorced.

5. Which is the correct way to write the underlined part of sentence 7?

   Ⓐ young age, and she

   Ⓑ young age; and she

   Ⓒ young age: and she

   Ⓓ Leave as is.

6. Which sentence should Manuel add after sentence 8 to support the ideas in the paragraph?

   Ⓕ Kenya is located in Africa.

   Ⓖ Anthropology became her new interest.

   Ⓗ He encouraged her interest in animal behavior.

   Ⓙ Anthropologists study the development of humans.

7. Which is the best way to express the meaning of the underlined words in sentence 10?

   Ⓐ wanting

   Ⓑ studying

   Ⓒ looking at

   Ⓓ taking care of

8. Which sentence is **not** related to the main idea of paragraph 3?

   Ⓕ sentence 8

   Ⓖ sentence 10

   Ⓗ sentence 12

   Ⓙ sentence 13

9. Which is the most effective substitution for the underlined word in sentence 16?

   Ⓐ witness

   Ⓑ witnessed

   Ⓒ is witnessing

   Ⓓ Leave as is.

10. Which transition should Manuel add to the beginning of sentence 20 to show a connection to the previous sentence?

   Ⓕ Today

   Ⓖ Finally

   Ⓗ Someday

   Ⓙ Consequently

11. Which is the correct way to spell the underlined word in sentence 20?

   Ⓐ compasionate

   Ⓑ comppasionate

   Ⓒ commpasionate

   Ⓓ Leave as is.

12. Which is the correct word to replace the underlined word in sentence 21?

   Ⓕ their

   Ⓖ there

   Ⓗ theyre

   Ⓙ Leave as is.

GO ON

Name _____

Date _____

Directions: Read the writing prompt. Write your composition on separate sheets of paper. Use the checklist to make sure that you do your best work.

Writing Prompt

Write an essay about what you think you will be doing on this exact day five years from now.

Checklist

- ❏ Write about all parts of the prompt.
- ❏ Present a clear central idea, and stay focused on it.
- ❏ Organize your composition from its introduction to its conclusion.
- ❏ Use transitions to connect your thoughts for the reader.
- ❏ Present meaningful ideas, and support them with specific information.
- ❏ Use appropriate words and a variety of sentence structures.
- ❏ Proofread and edit your writing for grammar, usage, mechanics, and spelling.

DONE!

TEACHER USE ONLY

Use the Good Writing Traits Rubric on pages 11a–b to score each trait. Transfer the score to the Student Profile form on page 8 in the Written Composition Rubric Scores column to factor them into the overall benchmark test score.

Focus and Unity	1	2	3	4
Organization	1	2	3	4
Idea Development	1	2	3	4
Voice and Style	1	2	3	4
Written Conventions	1	2	3	4

Student Profile: Narrative Writing

1) Use the answer key on page 103 to score the multiple-choice items. Circle the item number of each correct answer below. Multiple-choice items are worth one point each.

2) Use the Good Writing Traits Rubric on pages 11a–b to score the written composition. Circle the number of points earned for each writing trait below.

3) For each trait, add the number of correct multiple-choice items to the number of rubric points awarded. These are your student's writing trait scores. For an overall writing score, add the trait scores together. For an overall percentage, divide the total number of points earned by 32.

Writing Traits	Multiple-Choice Item Numbers (1 point each)	Written Composition Rubric Scores	Test Scores by Trait and Overall
Focus & Unity	1 2	1 2 3 4	____/6
Organization	3 10	1 2 3 4	____/6
Idea Development	6 8	1 2 3 4	____/6
Voice & Style	4 7	1 2 3 4	____/6
Written Conventions	5 9 11 12	1 2 3 4	____/8
TOTALS	12 points	20 points	Overall Score ____/32 = ____ %

Name _____

Date _____

Reflective Writing

Directions: Jamal created the outline to organize ideas for his composition. Use his outline to answer questions 1–3. Mark your answers as shown in the sample.

Jamal's Outline

I. My older sister and I do not get along.

   A. She often gives me mean surprises.

      1. She put leftover mashed potatoes in my shoes.

      2. She drew a moustache on my face when I fell asleep in front of the TV.

II. I got sick with the chicken pox.

   A. My mom had to work over-time at the hospital that week.

   B. I was miserable and had no one to take care of me.

      1. I was too tired to get out of bed.

      2. I was itching all over my body.

III. My sister had a different kind of surprise for me.

   A. My sister came home for lunch.

      1. She brought me lotion that soothed my itching.

      2. _____ **2** _____ .

Sample

Based on Jamal's outline, what type of composition is he planning to write?

Ⓐ persuasive

Ⓑ literary analysis

Ⓒ narrative

Ⓓ reflective *(marked)*

1. Which is the best title for Jamal's composition?

   Ⓐ My Sister is Full of Surprises

   Ⓑ Sick and Alone

   Ⓒ How to Cure the Chicken Pox

   Ⓓ Me and My Sister

2. Which detail goes on the blank line in Jamal's outline?

   Ⓕ I could not wait until my mom got home.

   Ⓖ My sister hid my book bag one morning.

   Ⓗ My sister made me chicken noodle soup.

   Ⓙ I thought I was too old to get chicken pox.

3. Based on the outline, how many paragraphs will Jamal's composition have?

   Ⓐ 1

   Ⓑ 3

   Ⓒ 7

   Ⓓ 13

GO ON ➡

Directions: Roselia wrote the composition about conquering her fear of singing in front of people. It is her first draft, and she wants you to help her improve it. Read her composition and answer questions 4–12.

Conquering My Fear

(1) New experiences can be scary, but they can also teach us a lot. (2) I love to sing. (3) I have always been terrified of singing in front of a crowd. (4) I thought I would never have the courage to perform in front of an audience.

(5) Last fall my friend Stefanie suggested I try out for the school musical. (6) Stefanie has been performing for as long as I have known her, so I hardly believed her when she said she still gets nervous when she sings in public. (7) I have known her since sixth grade. (8) She said she would give me tips about overcoming stage fright and promised to rehearse a song with me. (9) Patiently and thoughtfully, Stefanie helped me prepare for my audition. (10) I practiced my favorite song from the radio until I knew it so well that I could sing it in my sleep! (11) We talked about the lyrics so that I could sing the song better. (12) Stefanie also showed me how to look confident, whether I really felt it or really didn't feel it.

(13) The day of the audition came. (14) I did not care whether or not I got a part; I just wanted to make it threw the audition. (15) When my name was called, I confidently glided onto center stage. (16) Standing under the hot lights, my eyes squinted, searching for Stefanie in the audience. (17) Seeing her smile helped me relax. (18) I started out a little shaky however I just let the song carry me away. (19) In the end, I gave a pretty good audition and got a part in the musical! (20) I was even going to get to sing a solo!

(21) This thing taught me that it's normal to be nervous when performing. (22) Now that I have taken a chance on something I thought I could never do, who knows what else I am capable of!

GO ON ➡

4. Which transition should Roselia add to the beginning of sentence 3 to show a connection to the previous sentence?

   Ⓕ Finally

   Ⓖ However

   Ⓗ Therefore

   Ⓙ Consequently

5. Which is the correct way to spell the underlined word in sentence 8?

   Ⓐ reherse

   Ⓑ reherce

   Ⓒ rehearce

   Ⓓ Leave as is.

6. Which sentence is **not** related to the main idea of paragraph 2?

   Ⓕ sentence 5

   Ⓖ sentence 7

   Ⓗ sentence 10

   Ⓙ sentence 11

7. Which is the best way to write the underlined part of sentence 12?

   Ⓐ whether I felt it

   Ⓑ whether I felt it or not

   Ⓒ whether I felt it or did not

   Ⓓ whether I felt it or did not feel it

8. Which is the correct word to replace the underlined word in sentence 14?

   Ⓕ true

   Ⓖ trough

   Ⓗ through

   Ⓙ Leave as is.

9. Which is the correct way to write the underlined part of sentence 16?

   Ⓐ eyes squinting

   Ⓑ I squinted my eyes

   Ⓒ my eyes were squinting

   Ⓓ Leave as is.

10. Which is the correct way to punctuate the underlined part of sentence 18?

   Ⓕ shaky; however I

   Ⓖ shaky, however, I

   Ⓗ shaky; however, I

   Ⓙ Leave as is.

11. Which sentence should Roselia add after sentence 20 to conclude paragraph 3?

   Ⓐ I am now really looking forward to performing on stage.

   Ⓑ I am so happy that Stefanie was there to watch me.

   Ⓒ Singing a solo means that I will be singing all by myself.

   Ⓓ Singing a solo is making me feel nervous all over again.

12. Which is the most precise way to express the meaning of the underlined word in sentence 21?

   Ⓕ time

   Ⓖ confidence

   Ⓗ song

   Ⓙ experience

GO ON ➡

Name _____

Date _____

Directions: Read the writing prompt. Write your composition on separate sheets of paper. Use the checklist to make sure that you do your best work.

Writing Prompt

The American poet Maya Angelou said, "People will forget what you said, people will forget what you did, but people will never forget how you made them feel."

Think about what Maya Angelou said. Do you agree with her statement?

Write an essay about what you think of Maya Angelou's statement. Explain why you agree or disagree with her. Be sure to support your opinion with examples.

Checklist

- ❏ Write about all parts of the prompt.
- ❏ Present a clear central idea, and stay focused on it.
- ❏ Organize your composition from its introduction to its conclusion.
- ❏ Use transitions to connect your thoughts for the reader.
- ❏ Present meaningful ideas, and support them with specific information.
- ❏ Use appropriate words and a variety of sentence structures.
- ❏ Proofread and edit your writing for grammar, usage, mechanics, and spelling.

DONE!

TEACHER USE ONLY

Use the Good Writing Traits Rubric on pages 11a–b to score each trait. Transfer the score to the Student Profile form on page 10 in the Written Composition Rubric Scores column to factor them into the overall benchmark test score.

Focus and Unity	1	2	3	4
Organization	1	2	3	4
Idea Development	1	2	3	4
Voice and Style	1	2	3	4
Written Conventions	1	2	3	4

Name _____

Date _____

Student Profile: Reflective Writing

1) Use the answer key on page 103 to score the multiple-choice items. Circle the item number of each correct answer below. Multiple-choice items are worth one point each.

2) Use the Good Writing Traits Rubric on pages 11a–b to score the written composition. Circle the number of points earned for each writing trait below.

3) For each trait, add the number of correct multiple-choice items to the number of rubric points awarded. These are your student's writing trait scores. For an overall writing score, add the trait scores together. For an overall percentage, divide the total number of points earned by 32.

Writing Traits	Multiple-Choice Item Numbers (1 point each)	Written Composition Rubric Scores	Test Scores by Trait and Overall
Focus & Unity	1 2	1 2 3 4	____/6
Organization	3 4	1 2 3 4	____/6
Idea Development	6 11	1 2 3 4	____/6
Voice & Style	7 12	1 2 3 4	____/6
Written Conventions	5 8 9 10	1 2 3 4	____/8
TOTALS	12 points	20 points	Overall Score ____/32 = ____%

Good Writing Traits

Score	Focus and Unity	Organization	Development of Ideas	Voice and Style	Written Conventions	Extension (see next page)
4	**Initial Focus:** Establishes a specific central idea about the topic. **Unity:** Individual paragraphs and the writing as a whole are focused on the controlling idea.	**Structure:** Effectively organizes the writing as a whole and each paragraph according to its purpose. **Coherence:** Leads the reader through ideas and support in an orderly way and with effective transitions.	**Content Quality:** Presents meaningful ideas in an interesting and engaging way. **Elaboration:** Thoroughly explains and supports ideas with relevant and specific information.	**Reader Engagement:** Fully engages the reader with an individual voice and style. Tone is consistent. **Words and Sentences:** Words are precise and effective. Sentences are varied and flow together effectively.	**Grammar and Usage:** Sentences are complete and correct. Fragments, if present, are used intentionally. **Mechanics and Spelling:** Demonstrates consistent control with few or no errors.	All or most of the features of the type of writing are present.
3	**Initial Focus:** Establishes a central idea about the topic. **Unity:** Individual paragraphs and the writing as a whole are mostly focused on the controlling idea.	**Structure:** Generally organizes the writing according to its purpose. **Coherence:** Leads the reader through most ideas and support in an orderly way and with adequate transitions.	**Content Quality:** Presents ideas in an interesting way. **Elaboration:** Adequately explains and supports most ideas with relevant information.	**Reader Engagement:** Mostly engages the reader with an individual voice and style. Tone is mostly consistent. **Words and Sentences:** Most words are precise and effective. Most sentences are varied and flow together.	**Grammar and Usage:** Most sentences are complete and correct. **Mechanics and Spelling:** Demonstrates control with minor errors.	Some of the features of the type of writing are present.
2	**Initial Focus:** Includes an overly general idea about the topic. **Unity:** Individual paragraphs and the writing as a whole are somewhat focused on the general idea.	**Structure:** Organizes the writing, but not according to its purpose. **Coherence:** Leads the reader through some ideas and support in an orderly way with a few transitions.	**Content Quality:** Presents ideas, but in an uninteresting way. **Elaboration:** Briefly explains and/or minimally supports some ideas.	**Reader Engagement:** Somewhat engages the reader, but the voice and style are not unique. **Words and Sentences:** Some words are effective. Some sentences are varied, but the flow could be smoother.	**Grammar and Usage:** Some sentences are complete and correct. **Mechanics and Spelling:** Demonstrates little control with frequent errors.	Few of the features of the type of writing are present.
1	**Initial Focus:** Addresses the topic too broadly. **Unity:** Individual paragraphs and the writing as a whole lack focus.	**Structure:** Lacks organization. **Coherence:** Ideas and support, if present, lack order and transitions.	**Content Quality:** Lacks clear ideas. **Elaboration:** Lacks explanation and support.	**Reader Engagement:** Does not engage the reader. **Words and Sentences:** Words are often vague. Sentences lack variety and do not flow together.	**Grammar and Usage:** Errors create a barrier to understanding. **Mechanics and Spelling:** Errors create a barrier to understanding.	Very few, if any, of the features of the type of writing are present.

Good Writing Traits

Type of Writing	Focus and Unity	Organization	Development of Ideas	Voice and Style	Written Conventions
Expository	Focuses on and explains a central idea or thesis.	Uses one or a combination of organizational patterns in an appropriate way for the purpose and intended audience.	Elaborates with explanations, details, examples, facts, statistics, and reasons. Anticipates and addresses reader questions and expectations.	Uses a voice and style that are appropriate to the purpose and intended audience.	Uses standard English conventions.
Persuasive	Focuses on and defends a position or argument.	Some Organizational Patterns: • Spatial • Chronological • General to specific • Specific to general • Most important to least important	Elaborates with logical reasons, explanations, details, examples, facts, and statistics; establishes credibility; and appeals to the logic and emotion of the reader. Anticipates and addresses reader questions, concerns, expectations, biases, and counter-arguments.		
Literary Analysis	Focuses on the significant ideas and stylistic devices of one or more literary works.	• Least important to most important • Enumeration • Classification	Elaborates interpretations with support from the literary and other works.		
Narrative	Focuses on and relates a sequence of events.	• Illustration • Definition • Analysis • Comparison and contrast • Question and answer • Cause and effect	Elaborates with elements of imaginative text such as plot, character, setting, dialogue, conflict, and suspense to engage the reader. Elaborates with concrete sensory details and figurative language to help the reader form a mental picture.		
Reflective	Focuses on and expresses thoughts and feelings.	• Problem and solution • Hypothesis and results	Elaborates with details that convey thoughts and feelings and represents features of a personal history.		

Class Record Form

STUDENT NAME	Expository Writing Date _____	Persuasive Writing Date _____	Literary Analysis Date _____	Narrative Writing Date _____	Reflective Writing Date _____

Name _____

Date _____

Prewriting Test

Directions: This test takes you through the prewriting process. Answer questions 1–8 to help you plan a composition.

A. Topic

1. The five topics below are very broad. Put a ✔ next to the topic you will narrow.

Broad Topics: ☐ Food ☐ People ☐ Feelings ☐ Places ☐ Fun

2. Narrow your topic by writing in the inverted triangle. Make the topic narrow enough to write a composition about it.

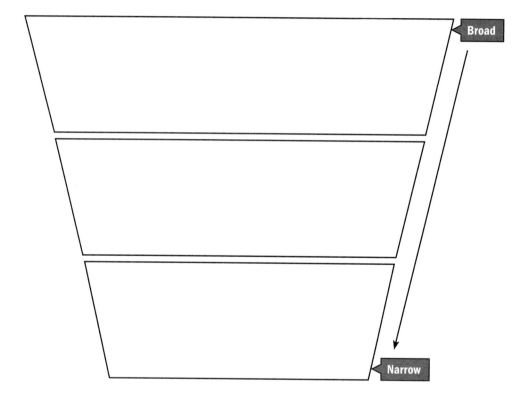

Name _____

Date _____

B. Audience and Tone

3. Who will be the audience for your composition?

_____

_____

4. Put a ✔ next to the best tone to use with your audience.

❑ very informal   ❑ somewhat informal   ❑ somewhat formal   ❑ very formal

C. Purpose and Form

5. What is the purpose of your composition?

_____

_____

6. What is the best form to use for your purpose?

_____

_____

7. Write the form, audience, topic, and purpose of your composition in the FATP chart.

Form: _____

Audience: _____

Topic: _____

Purpose: _____

Name _____

Date _____

D. Graphic Organizer

8. Use the space below to plan your composition with a graphic organizer. Choose a graphic organizer based on your form, audience, topic, and purpose.

DONE!

TEACHER USE ONLY

Use the Prewriting rubric on page 14 to score A-D. Circle the scores in the score box to the right. For the overall percent score, divide the number of points earned by 16.

A. Topic	1	2	3	4
B. Audience and Tone	1	2	3	4
C. Purpose and Form	1	2	3	4
D. Graphic Organizer	1	2	3	4
Overall Percent	___ Points / 16 = ___ %			

Prewriting Rubric

Use this rubric to score the Prewriting Test. Record the scores in the score box at the end of the test.

Score	A. Topic	B. Audience & Tone	C. Purpose & Form	D. Graphic Organizer
4	The topic is narrow enough for a composition.	The audience is plausible and the tone appropriate to the audience.	The purpose is plausible and the form appropriate to the purpose.	The graphic organizer is appropriate to the FATP and is completed in a clear and organized way.
3	The topic is narrowed, but it remains somewhat broad for a composition.	The audience is plausible and the tone mostly appropriate to the audience.	The purpose is plausible and the form mostly appropriate to the purpose.	The graphic organizer is appropriate to the FATP and is mostly complete, clear, and organized.
2	The topic is narrowed slightly, but it is too broad for a composition.	The audience is somewhat plausible and the tone somewhat appropriate to the audience.	The purpose is somewhat plausible and the form somewhat appropriate to the purpose.	The graphic organizer is somewhat appropriate to the FATP, but it is incomplete, unclear, and/or poorly organized.
1	A broad topic is chosen, but it is not narrowed.	The audience is implausible, and/or the tone is inappropriate.	The purpose is implausible, and/or the form is inappropriate.	The graphic organizer is inappropriate, incomplete, unclear, and/or poorly organized.

Name _____

Date _____

Drafting Test

Directions: Use the outline to draft a four-paragraph composition. Make sure that your introduction is engaging, that your paragraphs are organized, and that your conclusion is memorable. Write your draft on a separate sheet of paper.

I. Two types of vacations
    A. Relaxing: lie around and do nothing
    B. Active: travel to see and do new things
II. The relaxing vacation
    A. Stay at home
        1. Sleep late
        2. Watch TV or read
    B. Travel to a beach
        1. Lie in the sun
        2. Cool off in the water
III. The active vacation
    A. Road trip by car
        1. Drive to different states, like South Dakota
        2. See their attractions, like Mount Rushmore
    B. Amusement park
        1. Rides, like rollercoasters
        2. A lot of people
IV. Two types of vacations: relaxing and active
    A. My favorite type of vacation
    B. But any vacation is good to have

TEACHER USE ONLY

Use the Drafting rubric on page 16 to score the draft composition. Circle the scores in the score box to the right. For the overall percent score, divide the number of points earned by 16.

Introduction	1	2	3	4
Paragraph 2	1	2	3	4
Paragraph 3	1	2	3	4
Conclusion	1	2	3	4
Overall Percent	_____ Points / 16 = _____ %			

Drafting Rubric

Use this rubric to score the Drafting Test. Record the scores in the score box at the end of the test.

Score	Introduction	Paragraph 2	Paragraph 3	Conclusion
4	Introduction is engaging and introduces the main ideas of subsequent paragraphs.	Paragraph includes a topic sentence and details from the outline. It is focused, organized, coherent, and appropriate in tone.	Paragraph includes a topic sentence and details from the outline. It is focused, organized, coherent, and appropriate in tone.	Conclusion is memorable, summarizes main ideas, and gives final thoughts.
3	Introduction introduces the main ideas of subsequent paragraphs.	Paragraph includes a topic sentence and details from the outline. It is focused and organized.	Paragraph includes a topic sentence and details from the outline. It is focused and organized.	Conclusion summarizes main ideas.
2	Introduction states the topic.	Paragraph includes a topic sentence and details from the outline.	Paragraph includes a topic sentence and details from the outline.	Conclusion restates the topic.
1	Introduction does not state the topic.	Paragraph does not include a topic sentence. May list details.	Paragraph does not include a topic sentence. May list details.	Conclusion does not address the topic.

Name _____

Date _____

Revising Test

Directions: Bettina wrote the composition about the power of editing. It is her first draft, and she wants you to help her improve it. Read her composition and answer questions 1–4.

The Power of Editing

It was Tuesday night, the night before my research paper was due. I had spent weeks on that paper, and I wanted to read it one more time to make sure it was perfect.

I was checking to make sure that I had cited my sources correctly. I realized that I had used four sources. I needed five! My teacher is Mrs. Cho. She said that she would drop us a letter grade. If we didn't use five sources. I began to panic. The library was closed. I didn't have an Internet connection. How was I going to get my fifth source? I took a few deep breaths, I decided to go to the computer lab. I was going to go before Mrs. Cho's class. I was going to get my last source on the Internet.

The next morning, when I got to the lab, I had to ask the lab person, Ms. Turner, for something to access the Internet. I approached Ms. Turner, said hello, and asked her if I could use the Internet. She said yes, but she needed to fix something first. Instead of wasting my time waiting, I decided to proofread my paper until Ms. Turner was done. I changed lots of stuff in it. I became so involved proofreading, before I knew it, a bunch of time had passed. Time was running out, but Ms. Turner still had not finished. I sighed and accepted the fact that I had to turn my paper in as it was.

When I got my paper back from the teacher on Friday, her comment read, "Even though you are missing a source, I did not drop your grade. Your paper is so well written, I can tell you spent a lot of time editing your writing. Well done! Grade: A-." I was thrilled! The time I spent waiting for the Internet was time well spent.

Name _____

Date _____

1. Write three things you can tell about the narrator of the composition.

   _____

   _____

   _____

   _____

2. Name two things Bettina's composition made you want to know more about.

   _____

   _____

   _____

   _____

3. Describe two ways Bettina could improve the sentences in her second paragraph.
   Give an example of each.

   _____

   _____

   _____

   _____

4. Describe two ways Bettina could elaborate in her third paragraph. Give an example of each.

   _____

   _____

   _____

   _____

DONE!

TEACHER USE ONLY

Use the Revising rubric on page 18 to score questions 1–4. Circle
the scores in the score box to the right. For the overall percent
score, divide the number of points earned by 16.

	1	2	3	4
Question 1	1	2	3	4
Question 2	1	2	3	4
Question 3	1	2	3	4
Question 4	1	2	3	4
Overall Percent	___ Points / 16 = ___ %			

Revising Rubric

Use this rubric to score the Revising Test. Record the scores in the score box at the end of the test.

Score	Question 1	Question 2	Question 3	Question 4
4	Writes three plausible things about the narrator.	Names two things that the student wants to know more about. Both are thoughtful and relevant.	Describes two ways to improve the sentences. Gives two examples.	Describes two ways to elaborate. Gives two examples.
3	Writes two plausible things about the narrator.	Names two things that the student wants to know more about. Only one is thoughtful and relevant.	Describes two ways to improve the sentences. Gives only one example.	Describes two ways to elaborate. Gives only one example.
2	Writes one plausible thing about the narrator.	Names one thing that the student wants to know more about. It is thoughtful and relevant.	Describes one way to improve the sentences. Gives an example. OR Describes two ways to improve the sentences. Gives no examples.	Describes one way to elaborate. Gives one example. OR Describes two ways to elaborate. Gives no examples.
1	Writes only implausible things about the narrator.	Names something irrelevant that the student wants to know more about.	Describes one way to improve the sentences. Gives no example.	Describes one way to elaborate. Gives no example.

Name _____

Date _____

Editing and Proofreading Test

Directions: Juan wrote the graduation speech on the next page. He wants you to edit and proofread it. Complete steps A–D to edit Juan's speech.

A. Checklist

Before you proofread Juan's speech, list the types of errors that you will look for.

_____ _____

_____ _____

_____ _____

_____ _____

_____ _____

B. Find Errors

Go to the next page. Underline as many of the errors as you can find in Juan's speech.

C. Fix Errors

Go back to the speech and correct the errors that you underlined. Mark your corrections directly on the passage.

D. List Errors

Finally, list the types of errors that Juan made in his speech.

_____ _____

_____ _____

_____ _____

_____ _____

GO ON ➡

Name _____

Date _____

Graduation Speech

Good evening ladies and gentlemen, fellow students, and faculty. I would like to thank them for coming here tonight.

As graduates, we face an incredible future. I asked some friends, "When you think of the future, what do you think of?" My friend Sophia replied, "Technology." She's right. There is many technological advances that we have yet to imagine. New technology that we cannot dream of today was commonplace for future generations. With the rapid change that technology brings, however, also comes responsibility. We will need to deal with the vast possibilities that technology will bring and we will need to deal with them responsibly.

In answer to my question, another friend replied, "Fear." We can all relate to fear of the unknown. Graduates, you're stepping into the unknown as you embark on a new phase in your lives. Families you are watching your sons and daughters grow into young adults. I urge you all to do the following be courageous, take bold steps, and continue to learn.

When I think about the future. I think of hope. Each one of us has the power to make a difference. Maybe we will make a difference in one person's life, a community, or a country. Even though we may find chalenges and disappointments, we must remember that in the bigger picture, hope can get us through. We all have a responsibility toward future generations to maintain hope. To quote the late Dr. Martin Luther king, Jr., We must accept finite disappointment, but never lose infinite hope.

A. Checklist	1	2	3	4
B. Find Errors	1	2	3	4
C. Fix Errors	1	2	3	4
D. List Errors	1	2	3	4
Overall Percent	____ Points / 16 = ____ %			

Editing and Proofreading Rubric

Use this rubric to score the Editing Test. Record the scores in the score box at the end of the test.

Score	A. Checklist	B. Find Errors	C. Fix Errors	D. List Errors
4	Lists at least the 4 major categories of conventions: grammar, usage, mechanics, and spelling.	Finds 9–10 of the 10 errors. See Editing and Proofreading Anchor Sample on page 20b.	Fixes 9–10 of the 10 errors. See Editing and Proofreading Anchor Sample on page 20b.	Lists all the types of errors in the passage.
3	Lists 3 of the 4 major categories of conventions: grammar, usage, mechanics, and spelling.	Finds 6–8 of the 10 errors. See Editing and Proofreading Anchor Sample on page 20b.	Fixes 6–8 of the 10 errors. See Editing and Proofreading Anchor Sample on page 20b.	Lists most of the types of errors in the passage.
2	Lists 2 of the 4 major categories of conventions: grammar, usage, mechanics, and spelling.	Finds 3–5 of the 10 errors. See Editing and Proofreading Anchor Sample on page 20b.	Fixes 3–5 of the 10 errors. See Editing and Proofreading Anchor Sample on page 20b.	Lists some of the types of errors in the passage.
1	Lists 1 of the 4 major categories of conventions: grammar, usage, mechanics, and spelling.	Finds 1–2 of the 10 errors. See Editing and Proofreading Anchor Sample on page 20b.	Fixes 1–2 of the 10 errors. See Editing and Proofreading Anchor Sample on page 20b.	Lists few of the types of errors in the passage.

Editing and Proofreading Anchor Sample

Graduation Speech

Good evening ladies and gentlemen, fellow students, and faculty. I would like to thank you for coming here tonight.

As graduates, we face an incredible future. I asked some friends, "When you think of the future, what do you think of?" My friend Sophia replied, "Technology." She's right. There are many technological advances that we have yet to imagine. New technology that we cannot dream of today will be commonplace for future generations. With the rapid change that technology brings, however, also comes responsibility. We will need to deal with the vast possibilities that technology will bring, and we will need to deal with them responsibly.

In answer to my question, another friend replied, "Fear." We can all relate to fear of the unknown. Graduates, you're stepping into the unknown as you embark on a new phase in your lives. Families, you are watching your sons and daughters grow into young adults. I urge you all to do the following: be courageous, take bold steps, and continue to learn.

When I think about the future, I think of hope. Each one of us has the power to make a difference. Maybe we will make a difference in one person's life, a community, or a country. Even though we may find challenges and disappointments, we must remember that in the bigger picture, hope can get us through. We all have a responsibility toward future generations to maintain hope. To quote the late Dr. Martin Luther King, Jr., "We must accept finite disappointment, but never lose infinite hope."

Name _____

Date _____

Publishing Test

Directions: Answer questions 1–4. If you need more room, use the back of the page.

1. Describe two ways you can publish your writing. Give an example of each way.

   _____

   _____

   _____

2. Describe two ways you can make your writing look better with graphics.
   Give an example of each way.

   _____

   _____

   _____

3. Write two questions to ask yourself when reflecting on your writing.
   Explain how asking each question will help your writing.

   _____

   _____

   _____

   _____

4. Describe two uses for a writing portfolio. What writing would you
   include for each use?

   _____

   _____

   _____

   _____

DONE!

TEACHER USE ONLY

Use the Publishing rubric on page 22 to score questions 1–4.
Circle the scores in the score box to the right. For the overall
percent score, divide the number of points earned by 16.

	1	2	3	4
Question 1	1	2	3	4
Question 2	1	2	3	4
Question 3	1	2	3	4
Question 4	1	2	3	4
Overall Percent	____Points / 16 = ____ %

Publishing Rubric

Use this rubric to score the Publishing Test. Record the scores in the score box at the end of the test.

Score	Question 1	Question 2	Question 3	Question 4
4	Describes two ways to publish writing. Gives an example for each.	Describes two ways to make writing look better with graphics. Gives an example for each.	Writes two questions and explains how each will help the writer.	Gives two uses for portfolios and describes contents of each.
3	Describes two ways to publish writing. Gives only one example.	Describes two ways to make writing look better with graphics. Gives only one example.	Writes two questions, but only explains how one will help the writer.	Gives two uses for portfolios, but only describes contents of one.
2	Describes two ways to publish writing. Does not give examples. OR Describes one way to publish writing. Gives one example.	Describes two ways to make writing look better with graphics. OR Describes one way to make writing look better with graphics. Gives one example.	Writes two questions without explanation. OR Writes one question with an explanation.	Gives two uses without describing contents. OR Gives one use and describes contents.
1	Describes one way to publish writing.	Describes one way to make writing look better with graphics.	Writes one question.	Gives one use.

22

Name _____

Date _____

Chapter Test: Form A

Directions: For question **1**, order the stages of the writing process from **1 to 5** on the lines below.

1. Stages of the writing process:

   ___ Publishing

   ___ Editing/Proofreading

   ___ Drafting

   ___ Revising

   ___ Prewriting

Directions: For questions **2–10**, mark your answer as shown in the sample.

Sample

During which stage of the writing process should a writer check for spelling errors?

Ⓐ drafting

Ⓑ prewriting

Ⓒ publishing

Ⓓ editing/proofreading

2. During which stage of the writing process should a writer add graphics to a composition?

   Ⓐ revising

   Ⓑ drafting

   Ⓒ prewriting

   Ⓓ publishing

3. When editing and proofreading, a writer should

   Ⓕ narrow the focus of the topic.

   Ⓖ check for correct punctuation.

   Ⓗ determine the purpose for writing.

   Ⓙ consider changing the intended audience.

4. A writer should use transitional words and phrases to make a composition

   Ⓐ factual and truthful.

   Ⓑ exciting and colorful.

   Ⓒ clear and easy to read.

   Ⓓ convincing and persuasive.

5. When would a graphic organizer be most helpful to a writer?

   Ⓕ after making revisions

   Ⓖ before creating a draft

   Ⓗ when choosing an audience

   Ⓙ during the proofreading process

6. When revising, how should a writer share a composition?

   Ⓐ enter it to win a writing contest

   Ⓑ give it to other people for feedback

   Ⓒ send it to a magazine for publication

   Ⓓ read it to a crowd at an open-mike night

GO ON ➡

Name _____

Date _____

7. A writer should create a draft in order to

(F) capture ideas in writing.

(G) narrow the focus of a topic.

(H) decide how best to organize ideas.

(J) provide material for a graphic organizer.

8. Read the FATP chart.

Form: _essay_

Audience: _students, faculty, and parents_

Topic: _pros and cons of home schooling_

Purpose: _to inform_

Which type of essay would be most appropriate for the topic and purpose?

(A) persuasive

(B) descriptive

(C) cause and effect

(D) compare and contrast

9. When revising, a writer should

(F) send the composition to a magazine.

(G) add interesting details and examples.

(H) choose an audience for the composition.

(J) use a graphic organizer to organize ideas.

10. During which stage of the writing process should a writer make a composition look its best?

(A) drafting

(B) revising

(C) publishing

(D) prewriting

(**DONE!**)

Number Correct	x 10 =	Percent Score
_____	x 10 =	_____ %

Name _____

Date _____

Chapter Test: Form B

Directions: For question **1**, order the stages of the writing process from **1** to **5** on the lines below.

1. Stages of the writing process:

   ___ Revising

   ___ Publishing

   ___ Editing/Proofreading

   ___ Prewriting

   ___ Drafting

Directions: For questions **2–10**, mark your answer as shown in the sample.

Sample

During which stage of the writing process should a writer check for spelling errors?

Ⓐ drafting

Ⓑ prewriting

Ⓒ publishing

🅓 editing/proofreading

2. During which stage of the writing process should a writer gather facts?

   Ⓐ revising

   Ⓑ drafting

   Ⓒ prewriting

   Ⓓ publishing

3. Which statement about drafting is true?

   Ⓕ You should write a draft all in one sitting.

   Ⓖ It is okay to skip prewriting and start drafting.

   Ⓗ As you write a draft, you have to stick to your plan.

   Ⓙ You should use a pencil and lined notebook paper for a draft.

4. When would a thesaurus be most helpful to a writer?

   Ⓐ drafting

   Ⓑ revising

   Ⓒ prewriting

   Ⓓ publishing

5. Which would a writer do during the publishing stage of the writing process?

   Ⓕ send a composition to a magazine

   Ⓖ add interesting details and examples

   Ⓗ use a graphic organizer to organize ideas

   Ⓙ replace general words with specific words

6. During which stage of the writing process might it be helpful to read a composition backward?

   Ⓐ drafting

   Ⓑ revising

   Ⓒ publishing

   Ⓓ editing/proofreading

GO ON ➡

Name _____

Date _____

7. Read the FATP chart.

Form: _essay_

Audience: _students, faculty, and parents_

Topic: _the impact war has on art_

Purpose: _to inform_

Which type of essay would be most appropriate for the topic and purpose?

Ⓕ persuasive

Ⓖ descriptive

Ⓗ cause and effect

Ⓙ compare and contrast

8. During the publishing stage of the writing process, a computer helps a writer to

Ⓐ organize a composition.

Ⓑ check a composition for errors.

Ⓒ make a composition look good.

Ⓓ find facts to use in a composition.

9. Using facts and examples helps a writer to

Ⓕ prove a point.

Ⓖ hook a reader.

Ⓗ organize ideas.

Ⓙ express feelings.

10. When revising, a writer should

Ⓐ choose an audience for the composition.

Ⓑ replace general words with specific words.

Ⓒ use a graphic organizer to organize ideas.

Ⓓ send the composition to a newspaper or magazine.

_____ **DONE!** _____

Number Correct	x 10 =	Percent Score
_____	x 10 =	_____ %

Chapter 1

The Writing Process

STUDENT NAME	Test: Prewriting Date	Test: Drafting Date	Test: Revising Date	Test: Editing Date	Test: Publishing Date	Chapter Test A Date	Chapter Test B Date

Name _____

Date _____

Focus and Unity Test

Directions: Read the writing prompt. Write your composition on separate sheets of paper. Use the checklist to make sure that your writing is focused and unified.

Writing Prompt

New technology has changed the way people interact with each other.

Write a composition about some aspect of technology, and explain how it has changed the way people interact.

Checklist

❑ My composition presents a clear central idea.

❑ The main idea of each paragraph goes with the central idea of my composition.

❑ The main idea and details within each paragraph are related.

❑ The conclusion is about the central idea.

TEACHER USE ONLY	Rubric Score	1	2	3	4
Use the Focus and Unity rubric and anchor samples on pages 27a–c to score the composition. Circle the score in the score box to the right.	Percent Score	25%	50%	75%	100%

Focus and Unity Rubric

Use this rubric to score the composition written for the Focus and Unity Test. Record the score in the score box at the end of the test.

Score	Focus and Unity	
	How clearly does the writing present a central idea, opinion, or thesis?	**How well does everything go together?**
4 Wow!	The writing expresses a clear central idea or opinion about the topic.	Everything in the writing goes together. • The main idea of each paragraph goes with the central idea of the paper. • The main idea and details within each paragraph are related. • The conclusion is about the central idea.
3 Aaah.	The writing expresses a generally clear central idea or opinion about the topic.	Most parts of the writing go together. • The main idea of most paragraphs goes with the central idea of the paper. • In most paragraphs, the main idea and details are related. • Most of the conclusion is about the central idea.
2 Hmmm.	The writing includes a topic, but the central idea or opinion is not clear.	Some parts of the writing go together. • The main idea of some paragraphs goes with the central idea of the paper. • In some paragraphs, the main idea and details are related. • Some of the conclusion is about the central idea.
1 Huh?	The writing includes many topics and does not express one central idea or opinion.	The parts of the writing do not go together. • Few paragraphs have a main idea, or the main idea does not go with the central idea of the paper. • Few paragraphs contain a main idea and related details. • None of the conclusion is about the central idea.

Focus and Unity Anchor Samples

Score	Anchor Samples
4 Wow!	Over the years, technology continues to change. People are always finding new ways to interact with one another. Each new idea makes life a little easier for us. One example is computers. When I was younger, there was hardly anything you could really do with a computer. Then e-mail came along. It allowed you to keep in touch with people who maybe had moved or are far away. You can write them messages and even send pictures. It also helps in offices and workplaces if you need to send someone a document or a paper. For instance, my sister goes to college in Pomona, CA and sometimes she needs help on her papers. All she has to do is e-mail, and my mom can help her. A second example with computers is a program called AIM, short for AOL Instant Messenger. This allows you to have conversations online, so you don't have to call them or even see them. Say if you need to know what your homework was in a class, you can just instant message someone for help. On AIM you can also send pictures, have a webcam so people can see you, and even a microphone so they can hear you. The last example is text messaging. Instead of calling someone if you have a quick question, you can text them. It saves me a lot of time. Or say you can't call that person at the time, you can still text them to tell them what you were going to say. Technology has definitely changed how we interact whether it's with computers, or phones. It used to be that you could only interact when you were actually with that person, but all that is different now!
3 Aaah.	Technology. It has corrupted and brought us together. Cell phones, Internet, computers, iPods, Bluetooth, television, etc. Technology has somewhat separated me from my family, yet it brings us closer. The computer. It can vary in size, shape, color, speed, strength, memory; it's very much like the brain. Every day when I get home, I rush upstairs and turn my PC on and log onto MySpace. After that, I barely see my family, for I instant message friends and call them after just seeing them a few moments before. As I realized the errors of my way, I find new age technology can be corruptive. Family. I spend quality time with them watching a new episode of some highly integral series found on NBC. Our television has to be our highlight of our weekdays. On the weekend, it might be an enjoyable movie at the theaters or a get together with some friends playing games on the XBox or Play Station. Now, technology can bring all people to interact with each other. Our interactions and relationships all depend on some base of technology and how we use it can alter it.

Focus and Unity Anchor Samples, continued

Score	Anchor Samples
2 Hmmm.	Technology has changed the way people interact with each other in a huge way. Before there were phones, you would either have to walk or write a note. Now since we have phones, we can just call people if you need to ask them a quick question instead of taking all of that time. And with computers, especially the Internet, that changed things in a huge way. Now people can write letters to people across the country and they'll get it right when you send it. It helps people with emergencies. Cell phones and phones help with emergencies if you need the ambulance. That's why so many passed away years ago. People died because they couldn't get to the hospital or get help fast enough. So technology has changed the world tremendously.
1 Huh?	Technology has changed in so many ways. It still amazes me how cell phones work. Even though the person is in a different country or state, it still works. One piece of technology that amazes me most is text messaging. How can you send a message to someone so far and have that person receive it in a matter of minutes? People can interact faster this way. Pretty soon they can make phones to where you can see people and talk to them at the same time. Technology is so great, but I think we rely on it too much.

Name _____

Date _____

Organization Test

Directions: Read the writing prompt. Write your composition on separate sheets of paper. Use the checklist to make sure that your writing is organized.

Writing Prompt

Some adults think that being a teenager is easy. Many teens think that adults do not realize the stress that teens experience. Often teens try to balance school, extracurricular activities, family, and sometimes work.

Write a composition about the struggles teens may have as they try to balance their daily lives.

Checklist

❑ My composition has a clear structure and is appropriate for my purpose.

❑ The ideas flow well from paragraph to paragraph.

❑ The ideas in each paragraph flow well from one sentence to the next.

❑ Meaningful and effective transitions connect ideas.

TEACHER USE ONLY	Rubric Score	1	2	3	4
Use the Organization rubric and anchor samples on pages 29a–c to score the composition. Circle the score in the score box to the right.	Percent Score	25%	50%	75%	100%

Organization Rubric

Use this rubric to score the composition written for the Organization Test. Record the score in the score box at the end of the test.

Score	Organization	
	Does the writing have a clear structure and is it appropriate for the writer's purpose?	**How smoothly do the ideas flow together?**
4 Wow!	The writing has a clear structure that is appropriate for the writer's purpose.	The ideas progress in a smooth and orderly way. • The ideas flow well from paragraph to paragraph. • The ideas in each paragraph flow well from one sentence to the next. • Meaningful and effective transitions connect ideas.
3 Aaah.	The writing has a structure that is generally clear and appropriate for the writer's purpose.	Most of the ideas progress in a smooth and orderly way. • Most of the ideas flow well from paragraph to paragraph. • Most of the ideas in each paragraph flow well from one sentence to the next. • Meaningful and effective transitions connect most of the ideas.
2 Hmmm.	The structure of the writing is not clear or not appropriate for the writer's purpose.	Some of the ideas progress in a smooth and orderly way. • Some of the ideas flow well from paragraph to paragraph. • Some of the ideas in each paragraph flow well from one sentence to the next. • Meaningful and effective transitions connect some of the ideas.
1 Huh?	The writing includes many topics and does not express one central idea or opinion.	Few or none of the ideas progress in a smooth and orderly way. The ideas in the paragraphs and sentences do not flow well together and are not connected with transitions.

Organization Anchor Samples

Score	Anchor Samples
4 **Wow!**	Being a teenager is not an easy thing to do. Teens are put under a lot of pressure every day. Some teens know how to deal with it and others don't. A lot of adults say they know what it was like when they were teens, but times have changed and it's different now than when they were kids. Also a lot of parents push their teen too hard and the teen becomes over-stressed and doesn't know how to handle it, and most of the time, that is when they start getting into trouble. One of the major things teenagers stress a lot over is school. They have trouble balancing out school with other activities or relationships. For example, parents a lot of time push their teen too hard to be perfect, and the teens will stress out and this causes problems for the teen. School for some is easy, but for others it is somewhat a challenge. It doesn't mean they're not smart, just that they probably have a tough time balancing their life out. Another reason teens stress out a lot is because of relationships. The relationships could be with a significant other, family or even friends. If the teen is having a problem with some type of relationship, it can dramatically affect their lives, by stressing them out while they're at school or at home. When you have a relationship problem, you need to find out how to fix it, and if you can't, try not to think about it a lot, so it won't stress you out as bad. Parents also tend to push their teens too hard if the teen plays a sport. Sports should be a fun thing, not something to stress over. For instance, if the teen is always stressed and thinks about how good they need to be to please their parents, they will try too hard. In addition, some parents also think getting a job is more important than school because it brings money to the family. Parents will have their teen overworked and the teen will start to stress out. A job is a privilege you should have only when you get good grades in school. I definitely think parents don't fully understand how hard it is to be a teenager. They don't know everything about our lives and even if they did they can't help the way we feel. Teens don't stress out on purpose, teens hate being stressed out, and we would all appreciate it if our parents were more understanding.

Organization Anchor Samples, continued

Score	Anchor Samples
3 Aaah.	For some strange reason, many adults think that being a teenager is a breeze. As a teenager, I deeply disagree. Adults have no idea what goes on in their children's lives even though they like to believe they do. Even when teenagers say everything is fine, it's really not. School is a very stressful place, especially because of grades. The grades you get in high school determine what college you go to and what kind of job you have. There's six classes in a day, and sometimes you get stuck with four tests in just a few hours. If you get just one "C" on a test, then your whole grade will get lowered. That's quite depressing. It's quite impossible to prepare for four tests even if you do start studying straight after school. After all, school does take up about eight hours. Friends can be both good and bad for you, especially for girls and their mood swings. For some unexplainable reason, girls love to criticize each other behind each other's backs. Secrets get revealed by girls with big mouths. Then there's the familiar boyfriend stealing. How can teenagers deal with all that drama while juggling other things at the same time? Adults, such as parents, are probably the biggest stress factor for teens. Why do they have to nag all the time? Maybe the only problem is the parenting. Parents shouldn't try to pretend to know what's going on if they're not good actors.
2 Hmmm.	Some adults think being a teenager is easy, but they don't realize that it is not. When you're a teenager, you're under a lot of stress and pressure at home, at school, and within society. One of the things that adults expect from teens is a lot. They expect to do right in school, to do your chores, to finish your homework, and they don't realize that teens try to do their best at everything. Adults shouldn't expect everything from teens.
1 Huh?	A lot of teens like to get jobs because they want money to buy certain things that maybe their parents would get them. So it's hard for teens to balance their daily lives, especially with school. Other struggles that teens might have is dealing with their household because some households are stressful especially if you have little brothers or sisters. But it's hard when you have a job and you're going to school because if you work right after school, then by the time you get home at night you're too tired to do any homework.

Name _____

Date _____

Development of Ideas Test

Directions: Read the writing prompt. Write your composition on separate sheets of paper. Use the checklist to make sure that the ideas in your composition are well developed.

Writing Prompt

In the media we often see people working for a cause to better the world.

Write a composition about an important cause that citizens in our country should work to support. Explain why and how people could support this cause.

Checklist

❏ My composition engages the reader with worthwhile ideas and an interesting presentation.

❏ The ideas are well developed with important details and examples.

❏ My composition feels complete and will leave the reader satisfied.

TEACHER USE ONLY	**Rubric Score**	1	2	3	4
Use the Development of Ideas rubric and anchor samples on pages 31a–c to score the composition. Circle the score in the score box to the right.	**Percent Score**	25%	50%	75%	100%

Development of Ideas Rubric

Use this rubric to score the composition written for the Development of Ideas Test.
Record the score in the score box at the end of the test.

Score	Development of Ideas	
	How thoughtful and interesting is the writing?	**How well are the ideas explained and supported?**
4 Wow!	The writing engages the reader with worthwhile ideas and an interesting presentation.	**The ideas are fully explained and supported.** • The ideas are well developed with important details and examples. • The writing feels complete, and the reader is satisfied.
3 Aaah.	Most of the writing engages the reader with worthwhile ideas and an interesting presentation.	**Most of the ideas are explained and supported.** • Most of the ideas are developed with important details and examples. • The writing feels mostly complete, but the reader is left with some questions.
2 Hmmm.	Some of the writing engages the reader with worthwhile ideas and an interesting presentation.	**Some of the ideas are explained and supported.** • Only some of the ideas are developed. Details and examples are limited. • The writing leaves the reader with many questions.
1 Huh?	The writing does not engage the reader.	**The ideas are not explained or supported.** The ideas lack details and examples, and the writing feels incomplete.

Development of Ideas Anchor Samples

Score	Anchor Samples
4 **Wow!**	In the USA, almost everybody has a car. Everybody gives no thought to how the emissions from burning fossil fuels harm the air we breathe, the wildlife and flora around us, and the rising temperature of the Earth. This approach is wrong. Alternative and sustainable energy sources need to be adopted in the imminent future before the problem escalates into a global panic. The benefits are myriad for switching. Every power plant that produces energy through burning fossil fuels creates harmful atmosphere. In the US alone, disease and sickness related to poor air is on the rise. So far, the government has taken a largely neutral view of the issue, prolonging our dependence on such fuels until we must stop. By that point, there will be a prodigious amount of smog, acid rain, and pollutants destroying the health of humans and of flora and fauna. Humans aren't the only victims of pollution. Plants and animals suffer too from our carelessness and mismanagement. Many things can be done to curb emissions, yet due to an unwillingness to spend extra money to better the world, few things have been done. As a result, species are going extinct and more and more animals and plants are becoming threatened and endangered. It is worth preserving this diversity of life, and one of the first steps we can take is to discontinue our reliance on fossil fuels. Scientist aren't agreeing on the issue of global warming and its stated cause. Nonetheless, it is impossible to ignore the alarming trend of accelerating rates of temperature increases. By the end of the century, temperatures could be high enough to melt the icecaps of the poles and wipe many species of flora and fauna. A special type of eel has a harder time taking in oxygen as water temperature increases, so it'll literally suffocate from the heat. Climate is a hard thing to predict and model, but there is a lot of evidence pointing in the direction of global warming. Our dependence on fossil fuels has to terminate if we want to better the world. We need to think about developing solar, wind, geothermal, nuclear fusion, and other sources of alternative and sustainable energy. In the short term, everyone can contribute by using less energy and aiming for carbon neutral. More dollars need to be poured into making different energy sources economically viable. With everybody involved, this problem can be surmounted.

Development of Ideas Anchor Samples, continued

Score	Anchor Samples
3 Aaah.	In the media we often see people working for a cause to better the world. In my own opinion, I can only think of one important cause that citizens in our country should work to support. The cause that I think that citizens in our country should work to support is trying to decrease pollution. Pollution can in many ways affect our health and the things we eat. If people keep littering in the streets, and no one is able or going to clean it up, then eventually the streets will be flooded with trash. The sewers may be polluted as well as our water supply. If the trash is built up, it'll block roads and leave a strong smell in the air. Another way that pollution affects our health or food is that if the oceans are polluted then all of the fish and edible things in the oceans will die. So we aren't able to eat any food. Crops are grown by watering them, and if the water is polluted, and we aren't able to water them, we aren't able to obtain food, which affects our health. This is why it's important to see people working on decreasing pollution.
2 Hmmm.	People in our country need to work towards ending world hunger. Not just in our country but in the world. So many children in third world countries are dying from malnutrition, and nobody is helping them. So many children and even adults in this country don't stop to think about anyone other than themselves. Actually I know that parents use the saying, "Do you know that there are children out there starving?" We can set up simple organizations that could donate money or food. It isn't hard. Just think of all the things that people throw away that can still be used. All you have to do is think about someone else, not yourself.
1 Huh?	The citizens in our country should help support Africa. The reason I say that is because there are kids out there wanting to learn but they can't because they don't have schools. So we should make an effort to help those kids in Africa because it really would make a big difference in their lives.

Name _____

Date _____

Voice and Style Test

Directions: Read the writing prompt. Write your composition on separate sheets of paper. Use the checklist to make sure that your composition has voice and style.

Writing Prompt

Think of a person who has inspired you. The person may be anyone — a celebrity, an historical figure, a member of your family, even a character in a movie or a book.

Write a letter of appreciation to this person, and explain how he or she has inspired you.

Checklist

❏ My composition fully engages the reader with an individual voice and style.

❏ The tone of my composition is consistent throughout.

❏ The words are powerful and engaging.

❏ The sentences are varied and flow together effectively.

	Rubric Score	1	2	3	4
TEACHER USE ONLY Use the Voice and Style rubric and anchor samples on pages 33a–c to score the composition. Circle the score in the score box to the right.	**Percent Score**	25%	50%	75%	100%

Voice and Style Rubric

Use this rubric to score the composition written for the Voice and Style Test. Record the score in the score box at the end of the test.

Score	Voice and Style	
	Does the writing sound real and is it unique to the writer?	**Are the words and sentences interesting and appropriate to the purpose and audience?**
4 Wow!	The writing fully engages the reader with its individual voice and style. The tone is consistent throughout.	The words and sentences are interesting and appropriate to the purpose and audience. • The words are powerful and engaging. • The sentences are varied and flow together effectively.
3 Aaah.	Most of the writing engages the reader with a voice and style that are unique. The tone is mostly consistent.	Most of the words and sentences are interesting and appropriate to the purpose and audience. • Most words are powerful and engaging. • Most sentences are varied and flow together.
2 Hmmm.	Some of the writing engages the reader, but the voice and style are not unique.	Some of the words and sentences are interesting and appropriate to the purpose and audience. • Some words are powerful and engaging. • Some sentences are varied, but the flow could be smoother.
1 Huh?	The writing does not engage the reader.	Few or none of the words and sentences are appropriate to the purpose and audience. • The words are often vague and dull. • The sentences lack variety and do not flow together.

Voice and Style Anchor Samples

Score	Anchor Samples
4 Wow!	Dear Hugo, I am a mere mimic compared to you. All I have ever wanted to be was you. Hugo, my brother, you have been a great influence in my life. I cannot express or find the words to say how much your presence has influenced my life. It is ironic that we want to be like one another, what we both covet is found in one another, yet you don't realize what you possess is of great value. What we both possess is intangible. You are my inspiration. Even though I believed my life was bleak and blemished, now I see what you have seen within me. I have to say, with much love and benevolence that I love you, for you realized and made me realize that I am unique. I am "numero uno." So you see, you are my role model. One day I will be brave and unafraid of life and I will make myself proud, for that is what only matters. You have taught me this. With much love, Edgar
3 Aaah.	Dear Mom, There's always that one person in your life that always knows what to say or do to lift you up on your feet again, someone who inspires you to take chances and go for the goal. I just want to thank you for being my inspiration. You made me see that one person can do many things for someone they really care about. You've inspired me so many times as I was growing up, and still do. You showed me that there are people like you out there and I want to be like you too. I want to be able to make sacrifices and decisions that affect my welfare in so many ways. You've really had a powerful impact on what kind of person I want to be. So I want to thank you for everything you've done since I was born. I really appreciate everything, and I'll still be appreciating you throughout my life. Love, Kristen

Voice and Style Anchor Samples, continued

Score	Anchor Samples
2 Hmmm.	For My Hero: The person that has inspired me is a very young woman. She's my mom's friend's daughter. She has a very nice life because she didn't choose to ruin it like most girls do when they are young. She chose to study. She went all the way through college. She got married at a decent age, and now she has twins. She owns her own house and is very good with money. She is able to travel a lot. I think that she has had such a good life because she studied, worked hard, and didn't do what many teens do, like drugs, gangs fights, ditching. I also think her mom is and should be really happy for raising such a good daughter and now for having two cute grandsons. That's why she inspires me. She proves that you can have a good, fun, safe life. Humbly, R. C.
1 Huh?	Dear Mom and Dad, You guys have inspired me in many ways. Ever since I was little, I have looked up to both of you, and I just want to thank you for bringing me into this world with open arms, and I appreciate everything you guys have done for me, and how you have been there for me through our ups and downs we had. You inspired me by staying strong and not giving up, so I just wanted to say thank you. Love, Your daughter

Name _____

Date _____

Written Conventions Test

Directions: Read the writing prompt. Write your composition on separate sheets of paper. Use the checklist to make sure that your composition is error free.

Writing Prompt

When people find themselves in new environments or situations, they often have to change or adapt.

Write a composition about a time when you or someone you know had to change or adapt to a new environment or situation.

Checklist

- ❏ My sentences are complete and correct.
- ❏ Any sentence fragments are used on purpose to achieve an effect.
- ❏ My punctuation, capitalization, and spelling are correct.

TEACHER USE ONLY

Use the Written Conventions rubric and anchor samples on pages 35a–c to score the composition. Circle the score in the score box to the right.

Rubric Score	1	2	3	4
Percent Score	25%	50%	75%	100%

Written Conventions Rubric

Use this rubric to score the composition written for the Written Conventions Test.
Record the score in the score box at the end of the test.

Score	Written Conventions	
	Are the sentences written correctly?	**Does the writing show correct punctuation, capitalization, and spelling?**
4 Wow!	The sentences are complete and correct. Fragments may be used on purpose to achieve an effect.	The writing is free of major errors in punctuation, capitalization, and spelling.
3 Aaah.	<u>Most</u> of the sentences are complete and correct.	The writing has <u>some</u> errors in punctuation, capitalization, and spelling.
2 Hmmm.	<u>Few</u> of the sentences are complete and correct, but the reader can understand the meaning.	The writing has <u>many</u> errors in punctuation, capitalization, and spelling.
1 Huh?	The sentences are <u>not</u> complete and correct. The writing is difficult to read and understand.	The errors in punctuation, capitalization, and spelling make the writing difficult to read and understand.

Written Conventions Anchor Samples

Score	Anchor Samples
4 Wow!	Everyone knows that change is inevitable. There have been times in all our lives in which we were subjected to change and have adapted to new circumstances or environments. I can clearly remember it was really hard for me to adapt to my aunt moving in with my family. There were many changes that I endured when she first arrived. I was so used to only having four other people living with me: my mother, brother, sister-in-law, and niece. It was all so easy for me because we all kept to ourselves and never really tried to have much contact with each other. That all changed when my aunt came from Florida. She's very old, but also very active. She's always trying to talk to everyone, but we were all so used to just having small talk that we all got annoyed by her constant attempts to hold long conversations. Not only was it hard to adapt to her long talking sessions, it was also hard having her around. Period. Being so used to our calm, quiet house, it was hard to try and interact more with this new person. Although it was complicated, we somehow made a compromise and tried to make things less awkward for her. Although it's been about six months since she moved in, it's still kind of hard to just want to talk to her. The fact that she is old and occasionally aggravating makes us want to spend more time to ourselves than we did before she came. Adapting to having her live with us has been a major change for everyone. Changing certain things is unavoidable, so we have to try and make things work. Sometimes compromising is the only way to make things easier. Trying to make my aunt feel more at home was hard, but we've achieved it.
3 Aaah.	I could remember when I went to Idaho to live for a while, I had to adjust, because it was not like California, where I used to just waste everything. In Idaho, the family I stayed with was very conservative. In California I would take thirty minute showers just because it felt good in the warm water. When I went to Idaho, I had to take much shorter showers. The same water I used to shower in was the water that was used for the laundry. I also had to adapt to eating pancakes with no syrup because it was just a waste of money. The way of having fun was much different, too. There were no video games, but we still found many ways to have fun.

Written Conventions Anchor Samples, continued

Score	Anchor Samples
2 Hmmm.	When I am in a wrestling match I always have to change my position and adapt to my environment. I can never be in the same place for more than a seconds and if I am, that's when misteaks happen. Adapting is a must if you wanna be a wrestler. I get put in a variety of different situations and holds that I have to get out off or I will lose the match. Adapting is a nateral change that everyone goes through. At least one's in there life and it is useally a good thing.
1 Huh?	Yes I no how at fills to change to a new environment. Yes It can be hard to change but yes change is good but why dose it have to be so hard. Especially when you try to fit in at school. In my opinion the hardest think is to give up your old style you may not fit in at first so you become attacked to the new style. Giving up on your friends is hard especially. If you move all the way acres the world you loose contact with them. Then you some how will try to get new friends somehow.

Name _____

Date _____

Chapter Test: Form A

Directions: Ana wrote the composition about global warming. It is her first draft, and she wants you to help her improve it. Read her composition and answer questions 1–10.

Is Global Warming Melting Antarctica?

(1) Can you imagine a piece of ice the size of Rhode Island crashing into the sea?   (2) In 2002, that's exactly what happened in Antarctica. (3) A large ice shelf collapsed into the sea.   (4) It was called the Larsen B ice shelf.

(5) The Larsen B ice shelf was about 10,000 years old.   (6) Why did a huge piece of ice that lasted for so long suddenly melt?   (7) Scientists believe <u>its</u> destruction was caused by global warming.   (8) Global warming means that the Earth is heating up.   (9) Antarctica was the warmest in recorded history when Larsen B disappeared.   (10) Some people confuse Antarctica with the Arctic Circle.

(11) In 2002, a group of scientists watched in amazement as Larsen B tumbled into the sea.   (12) This unusual event made the scientists worry about other major ice shelves in Antarctica.   (13) They believe that global warming is putting the ice shelves in danger!   (14) Warmer temperatures are melting the ice, and pools of water are forming on the ice shelves.   (15) These pools of water are cracking and weakening the ice shelves.   (16) As the ice shelves become <u>weaker they</u> could break off into the sea.

(17) The scientists' concern is that if many ice shelves fall into the sea, sea-levels will rise.   (18) Higher sea-levels mean much of our land could be covered in water!   (19) Some people are moving away from coastal areas. (20) Although scientists believe that global warming is destroying ice shelves like the Larsen B, they say that global devastation will not happen <u>soon</u>. (21) As the scientists continue their research, <u>you</u> are learning ways we can slow down global warming and save our ice shelves.

Name _____

Date _____

Sample

What type of writing is Ana's composition?

Ⓐ a poem

🅑 a report

Ⓒ a memoir

Ⓓ a biography

1. Which is the **best** way to combine sentences 3 and 4?

   Ⓐ Larsen B, a large ice shelf, collapsed into the sea.

   Ⓑ Larsen B collapsed into the sea; it was a large ice shelf.

   Ⓒ A large ice shelf collapsed into the sea, and it was called Larsen B.

   Ⓓ Collapsing into the sea, it was a large ice shelf called the Larsen B.

2. In sentence 7, the word <u>its</u> should be changed to

   Ⓕ it

   Ⓖ it's

   Ⓗ its'

   Ⓙ No change

3. Which transition should be added to the beginning of sentence 9 to show a connection to the previous sentence?

   Ⓐ However

   Ⓑ Therefore

   Ⓒ For example

   Ⓓ In addition

4. Which sentence is off topic and should be removed from the second paragraph?

   Ⓕ Sentence 7

   Ⓖ Sentence 8

   Ⓗ Sentence 9

   Ⓙ Sentence 10

5. Which sentence should Ana add after sentence 16 to conclude the third paragraph?

   Ⓐ The ice shelves are cracking and weakening.

   Ⓑ Scientists think that this explains what happened to Larsen B.

   Ⓒ The pools of water do not freeze because of global warming.

   Ⓓ Scientists did not think that Larsen B could break.

GO ON ➡

36b

Name _____

Date _____

6. In sentence 16, the underlined portion should be changed to

- Ⓕ weaker, they
- Ⓖ weaker: they
- Ⓗ weaker; they
- Ⓙ No change

7. In sentence 20, which of these is the **most** precise way to express the word <u>soon</u>?

- Ⓐ too soon
- Ⓑ right away
- Ⓒ during this century
- Ⓓ for a really long time

8. In sentence 21, the word <u>you</u> should be changed to

- Ⓕ us
- Ⓖ they
- Ⓗ we
- Ⓙ No change

9. Which sentence is **not** related to the main idea of the last paragraph?

- Ⓐ sentence 17
- Ⓑ sentence 18
- Ⓒ sentence 19
- Ⓓ sentence 20

10. Which sentence should Ana add after sentence 21 to conclude the last paragraph?

- Ⓕ It is important for scientists to continue their research.
- Ⓖ Saving the ice shelves will help prevent rising sea levels.
- Ⓗ Global devastation may occur sooner than scientists think.
- Ⓙ If much of our land is covered in water, cities could be flooded.

DONE!

Number Correct	x 10 =	Percent Score
_____	x 10 =	_____ %

Chapter Test: Form B

Directions: Luis wrote the composition about Penelope, the robotic nurse. It is his first draft, and he wants you to help him improve it. Read his composition and answer questions 1–10.

Robots in the Operating Room

(1) When Penelope entered the operating room for the first time, she was not at all nervous.   (2) In fact, Penelope felt nothing at all. (3) Because Penelope is a robot!   (4) Dr. Michael R. Treat is a surgeon who helped create Penelope.   (5) In 2005, Dr. Treat watched Penelope help operate on a patient's arm.   (6) Penelope made medical history as the first robot to act as an independent surgical aide during an operation.

(7) Penelope is a one-armed robotic scrub nurse.   (8) She responds to voice commands from a surgeon.   (9) Penelope's computer brain "listens" for the surgeon's commands.   (10) When the surgeon asks for <u>something</u>, she repeats the word, and reaches for the tool.   (11) She then hands it to the surgeon with her mechanical arm.   (12) Penelope has a built-in digital camera that sees everything on the surgery table. (13) Her internal camera can identify surgical tools.   (14) Artificial intelligence software enables Penelope to count the <u>surgical tools so that none are lost.</u>   (15) Computer scientists have made remarkable progress in artificial intelligence.   (16) Penelope is also able to make predictions about what tool the surgeon will ask for next.   (17) After the surgeon uses the tools, Penelope then carefully puts them back in place.

(18) Although Penelope has made medical history, robots will not be replacing humans to do difficult tasks any time soon.   (19) Penelope is just one of many advances in modern medicine.   (20) Many supporters of surgical technology, such as Dr. Treat, say the use of independent surgical robots can free up medical staff to do jobs that require a personal touch.   (21) Penelope can help hand out the right tools in the operating room, but she can't make <u>patience</u> and families feel better.

Name _____

Date _____

Sample

What type of writing is Luis's composition?

Ⓐ a poem

🅑 a report

Ⓒ a memoir

Ⓓ a biography

---

1. Which is the **best** way to combine sentences 2 and 3?

Ⓐ In fact, Penelope felt nothing at all, and is a robot!

Ⓑ In fact, Penelope felt nothing at all because Penelope is a robot!

Ⓒ In fact, Penelope felt nothing at all, Penelope is a robot!

Ⓓ In fact, Penelope felt nothing at all, because a robot!

2. Which is the **best** way to combine sentences 7 and 8?

Ⓕ Responding to voice commands from a surgeon is Penelope, a one-armed robotic scrub nurse.

Ⓖ A one-armed robotic scrub nurse is Penelope, who responds to voice commands from a surgeon.

Ⓗ Penelope, a one-armed robotic scrub nurse she responds to voice commands from a surgeon.

Ⓙ Penelope is a one-armed robotic scrub nurse that responds to voice commands from a surgeon.

3. In sentence 10, which of these is the most precise way to express the meaning of the word <u>something</u>?

Ⓐ tools

Ⓑ things

Ⓒ a word

Ⓓ a scalpel

4. Which transition should be added to the beginning of sentence 12 to show a connection to the previous sentence?

Ⓕ However

Ⓖ Therefore

Ⓗ Furthermore

Ⓙ Consequently

5. In sentence 14, the underlined portion should be changed to

Ⓐ surgical tools: so that none are lost

Ⓑ surgical tools; so that none are lost

Ⓒ surgical tools, so that none are lost

Ⓓ No change

GO ON ➡

Name _____

Date _____

6. Which sentence is off topic and should be removed from the second paragraph?

   (F) sentence 14

   (G) sentence 15

   (H) sentence 16

   (J) sentence 17

7. Which sentence should Luis add after sentence 17 to conclude the second paragraph.

   (A) Her accurate predictions help the surgeon.

   (B) The surgeon does not need to replace the tools.

   (C) Penelope identifies the tools with her digital camera.

   (D) It is very important to account for all surgical instruments.

8. Which sentence is **not** related to the main idea of the last paragraph?

   (F) sentence 18

   (G) sentence 19

   (H) sentence 20

   (J) sentence 21

9. In sentence 21, the word patience should be changed to

   (A) pateints

   (B) patients

   (C) pateince

   (D) No change

10. Which sentence should Luis add after sentence 21 to conclude the last paragraph?

   (F) Penelope is not programmed to provide comfort.

   (G) People do not expect to see a robot in a hospital.

   (H) People still want to be comforted by other people, not robots.

   (J) Penelope cannot understand the needs of family members.

—————— (**DONE!**) ——————

Number Correct	x 10 =	Percent Score
_____	x 10 =	_____ %

Chapter 2

Good Writing Traits

STUDENT NAME	Test: Focus & Unity		Test: Organization		Test: Development of Ideas		Test: Voice & Style		Test: Written Conventions		Chapter Test A		Chapter Test B	
	Date		Date		Date		Date		Date		Date		Date	

Name _____

Date _____

Test: Writing Wanders

Directions: The writing wanders in the letter below. On a separate sheet of paper, rewrite the letter so that it is focused. Use the Solutions to help you revise.

Dear Principal Diaz:

I have heard that our school is thinking about buying a laptop for every student to use for school work. I think that is a great idea! It would be helpful for school in so many ways. We could take notes on a laptop. We could also IM friends in class. I hope they have a wireless Internet connection. I could even visit some friends on My Space. By the way, have you seen that You Tube video with the laughing hamster? Hilarious! I have a Mac at home.

Sincerely,

Josephine Ostas

Solutions:

- *Speak Your Truth:* Explain what you know in your heart.
- *Show Your Ideas in a Flow:* Use an idea organizer to map out your thoughts.

TEACHER USE ONLY	Rubric Score	1	2	3	4
Use the Writing Wanders rubric on page 40 to score the revision. Circle the score in the score box to the right.	Percent Score	25%	50%	75%	100%

Rubric and Anchor Samples: Writing Wanders

Use this rubric to score the test for Writing Wanders. Record the score in the score box at the end of the test.

Score	What to Look for	Anchor Samples
4 Wow!	**Everything in the writing goes together.** • The ideas stay on topic. • The details support the ideas.	I have heard that our school is thinking about buying a laptop for every student to use for school work. I think that is a great idea! It would be helpful for school in so many ways. Taking notes on a laptop would be a lot neater than my handwriting. Writing papers for English or History would be so much easier on a word processor. We would even have a calculator for math class. Finally, having a laptop to use daily will help students develop computer skills that will be helpful at college or work after graduation.
3 Aaah.	**Most parts of the writing go together.** • Most ideas stay on topic. • Most details support the ideas.	I have heard that our school is thinking about buying a laptop for every student to use for school work. I think that is a great idea! It would be helpful for school in so many ways. Taking notes on a laptop would be a lot neater than my handwriting. Writing papers for English or History would be so much easier on a word processor. I like History more than English and English more than Math. Finally, having a laptop to use daily will help students develop computer skills.
2 Hmmm.	**Some parts of the writing go together.** • Some ideas stay on topic. • Some details support the ideas.	I have heard that our school is thinking about buying a laptop for every student to use for school work. I think that is a great idea! It would be helpful for school in so many ways. We could take notes on a laptop. We could even use its calculator and spell-check. I hope they have a wireless Internet connection. I could even visit some friends on My Space. It would probably make it easier to write papers, too. These laptops have to be better than my computer at home.
1 Huh?	**The parts of the writing do not go together.** • Few ideas stay on topic. • Few details support the ideas.	I have heard that our school is thinking about buying a laptop for every student to use for school work. I think that is a great idea! It would be helpful for school in so many ways. We could take notes on a laptop. We could also IM friends in class. I hope they have a wireless Internet connection. I could even visit some friends on My Space. It would probably make it easier to write papers, too. I have a Mac at home.

Name _____

Date _____

Test: Can't Write Enough

Directions: There is not enough writing in the paragraph below. On a separate sheet of paper, rewrite the paragraph so that it has more details. Use the Solutions to help you revise.

The Start of a Bad Day

The cereal was gone, and I almost went without breakfast. I ate some of my mom's organic yogurt. It wasn't bad, and I did not starve.

Solutions:

- *Get into an Argument:* Imagine your response to someone who is arguing with you.
- *Prove It on Your Own:* Use the way you know things to add proof.
- Use *Ba-Da-Bings* to collect more details:

Where your feet were

What you saw

What you thought

TEACHER USE ONLY	Rubric Score	1	2	3	4
Use the Can't Write Enough rubric on page 42 to score the revision. Circle the score in the score box to the right.	Percent Score	25%	50%	75%	100%

Rubric and Anchor Samples: Can't Write Enough

Use this rubric to score the test for Can't Write Enough. Record the score in the score box at the end of the test.

Score	What to Look for	Anchor Samples
4 Wow!	**The ideas are fully explained and supported.** • The ideas are well developed with important details and examples. • The writing feels complete, and the reader is satisfied.	I walked into the kitchen this morning, ready for a big bowl of my favorite cereal. The box was empty, and I was sure I would starve. I opened the refrigerator door wide and looked at half-filled jars of jelly and moldy leftovers. Then, all of a sudden, one of my mom's containers of organic yogurt jumped out at me. "Why not?" I thought. Before I knew it, I had polished off all the yogurt. It was delicious, and now I'm a big fan of organic yogurt!
3 Aaah.	**Most of the ideas are explained and supported.** • Most of the ideas are developed with important details and examples. • The writing feels mostly complete, but the reader is left with some questions.	When I went to the kitchen this morning and saw that the cereal was gone, I thought I would go without breakfast. As I stood in front of the fridge, I did not see one appetizing thing for breakfast. I was sure I would go hungry. Then I saw one of my mom's containers of organic yogurt and thought, "Why not?" Before I knew it, I had eaten the whole thing!
2 Hmmm.	**Some of the ideas are explained and supported.** • Only some of the ideas are developed. Details and examples are limited. • The writing leaves the reader with many questions.	This morning, the cereal was gone and I almost went without breakfast. It looked like the fridge had absolutely nothing good to eat. Then I saw my mom's organic yogurt and decided to try it. It wasn't bad, and I did not have to miss breakfast.
1 Huh?	**The ideas are not explained or supported.** The ideas lack details and examples, and the writing feels incomplete.	The cereal was gone, and I almost went without breakfast. The fridge had absolutely nothing! Then I ate some of my mom's organic yogurt. It wasn't bad, and I did not starve.

Name _____

Date _____

Test: Writing Is Not Connected

Directions: The writing is not connected in the composition below. On a separate sheet of paper, rewrite the composition so that the ideas are connected. Use the Solutions to help you revise.

Friends for Life

Friendships are important. Friends help us through difficult times. They help us laugh, learn, and enjoy life.

We all will need good friends to help us through hard times. Carlos broke up with me and my friends were very supportive. When my friend Anita had to move, I helped her pack and threw her a goodbye party.

Friends are not just for rough times. They help us laugh and learn. I was struggling with History. My friend Simon gave me helpful study tips. Some of his techniques made me laugh, but they worked!

Friends help us through all of life's ups and downs. Some friendships will last a lifetime.

Solutions:

- *Take Time for Transitions:* Use transitions to signal how your ideas are related.
- *Connect Your Paragraphs:* Use transitions to tell your reader what to expect next.

	Rubric Score	1	2	3	4
TEACHER USE ONLY Use the Writing Is Not Connected rubric on page 44 to score the revision. Circle the score in the score box to the right.	**Percent Score**	25%	50%	75%	100%

Rubric and Anchor Samples: Writing Is Not Connected

Use this rubric to score the test for Writing Is Not Connected. Record the score in the score box at the end of the test.

Score	What to Look for	Anchor Samples
4 Wow!	**The ideas progress in a smooth and orderly way.** • The ideas flow well from paragraph to paragraph. • The ideas in each paragraph flow well from one sentence to the next. • Meaningful and effective transitions connect ideas.	Friendships are important. Sometimes friends help us through difficult times. Other times, they help us laugh, learn, and enjoy life. To begin with, we all will need good friends to help us through hard times. For instance, when Carlos broke up with me, my friends were very supportive. Likewise, when my friend Anita had to move, I helped her pack and threw her a goodbye party. However, friends are not just for rough times. They also help us laugh and learn. Once, when I was struggling with History, my friend Simon gave me helpful study tips. Some of his techniques made me laugh, but they worked! In summary, friends help us through all of life's ups and downs. And if you're lucky, some friendships will last a lifetime.
3 Aaah.	**Most of the ideas progress in a smooth and orderly way.** • Most of the ideas flow well from paragraph to paragraph. • Most of the ideas in each paragraph flow well from one sentence to the next. • Meaningful and effective transitions connect most of the ideas.	Friendships are important. Sometimes friends help us through difficult times. Other times, they help us laugh, learn, and enjoy life. To begin with, we all will need good friends to help us through hard times. When Carlos broke up with me, my friends were very supportive. When my friend Anita had to move, I helped her pack and threw her a goodbye party. However, friends are not just for rough times. They also help us laugh and learn. When I was struggling with History, my friend Simon gave me helpful study tips. Some of his techniques made me laugh, but they worked! In summary, friends help us through all of life's ups and downs. And if you're lucky, some friendships will last a lifetime.
2 Hmmm.	**Some of the ideas progress in a smooth and orderly way.** • Some of the ideas flow well from paragraph to paragraph. • Some of the ideas in each paragraph flow well from one sentence to the next. • Meaningful and effective transitions connect some of the ideas.	Friendships are important. Friends help us through difficult times. Other times, they help us laugh, learn, and enjoy life. We all will need good friends to help us through hard times. When Carlos broke up with me, my friends were very supportive. When my friend Anita had to move, I helped her pack and threw her a goodbye party. Friends are not just for rough times. They also help us laugh and learn. When I was struggling with History, my friend Simon gave me helpful study tips. Some of his techniques made me laugh, but they worked! Friends help us through all of life's ups and downs. And if you're lucky, some friendships will last a lifetime.
1 Huh?	**Few or none of the ideas progress in a smooth and orderly way.** The ideas in the paragraphs and sentences do not flow well together and are not connected with transitions.	Friendships are important. Friends help us through difficult times. They help us laugh, learn, and enjoy life. We all will need good friends to help us through hard times. When Carlos broke up with me, my friends were very supportive. When my friend Anita had to move, I helped her pack and threw her a goodbye party. Friends are not just for rough times. They help us laugh and learn. I was struggling with History. My friend Simon gave me helpful study tips. Some of his techniques made me laugh, but they worked! Friends help us through all of life's ups and downs. If you're lucky, some friendships will last a lifetime.

Name _____

Date _____

Test: Writing Is Too Vague

Directions: The writing is too vague in the paragraph below. On a separate sheet of paper, rewrite the paragraph so that it is clear and precise. Use the Solutions to help you revise.

My Shoes Lead an Active Life

Most shoes are boring, but not mine. My shoes like activity and excitement. They like to go places and play ball. My shoes dream of things like being in a big arena. My shoes are good because they do not like boring stuff.

Solutions:

- *Add Snapshots and Thoughtshots:* Describe in detail what you see and think.
- *Complete a Target Diagram:* Add layers and dimensions to your writing.
- *Use the Intensity Scale:* Use specific, precise words to say exactly what you mean.

VAGUE   **SHARP**

       general words   medium words   precise words

TEACHER USE ONLY	Rubric Score	1	2	3	4
Use the Writing Is Too Vague rubric on page 46 to score the revision. Circle the score in the score box to the right.	Percent Score	25%	50%	75%	100%

Rubric and Anchor Samples: Writing Is Too Vague

Use this rubric to score the test for Writing Is Too Vague. Record the score in the score box at the end of the test.

Score	What to Look for	Anchor Samples
4 Wow!	**The writing is clear and precise.** The writing contains precise words and sensory details.	Most people's shoes prefer to lounge in the comfort of their cozy living rooms, but my basketball shoes like to get out and go. They look for adventure down every unbeaten path in my neighborhood. Anytime there are people out on the court, my basketball shoes are there in a flash! My shoes dream big, too. They fantasize about running up and down the court at Madison Square Garden or even at the home of the Lakers—Staples Center! My basketball shoes keep me smiling because they thrive on constant activity, excitement and adventure.
3 Aaah.	<u>Most</u> **of the writing is clear and precise.** Most of the writing contains precise words and sensory details.	Most shoes don't like much action, but my basketball shoes like to get out and go. My basketball shoes love activity and adventure. They like to go along unbeaten paths and find places to play ball. My basketball shoes have dreams too. They would love to run up and down the courts of Madison Square Garden or Staples Center! My basketball shoes make me happy because they thrive on excitement.
2 Hmmm.	<u>Some</u> **of the writing is clear and precise.** Some of the writing contains precise words and sensory details.	Most shoes don't like much action, but my basketball shoes like to get out and go. My basketball shoes love activity and adventure. They like to go along unbeaten paths and find places to play ball. My shoes dream of things like playing in a big arena. My shoes are good because they live an exciting life.
1 Huh?	**The writing is <u>not</u> clear and precise.** The writing lacks precise words and sensory details.	Most shoes are boring, but not mine. My shoes like activity and excitement. They like to go places and play ball. My shoes dream of things like being in a big arena. My shoes are good because they want an exciting life.

Name _____

Date _____

Test: Writing Sounds Like a List

Directions: The writing sounds like a list in the paragraph below. On a separate sheet of paper, rewrite the paragraph so that it is more developed. Use the Solutions to help you revise.

An Uninvited Guest

Fernando, Kyoko, and I went camping. We chose a hidden camp site. We put up our tent and unpacked our food. We went on a hike to the lake. Then we returned to the campsite. When we got back, we heard something in our tent. A bear cub appeared. We went inside the car. We watched the cub feast on all our food. The cub left. We came out of the car. We quickly packed up our things and left. It was time to relocate.

Solutions:

- *Add Meat to the Bones:* Use dialogue, sensory details, snapshots, and thoughtshots.
- *Zero In on a Moment:* Concentrate on one important moment and give specific details.

TEACHER USE ONLY	Rubric Score	1	2	3	4
Use the Writing Sounds Like a List rubric on page 48 to score the revision. Circle the score in the score box to the right.	Percent Score	25%	50%	75%	100%

Rubric and Anchor Samples: Writing Sounds Like a List

Use this rubric to score the test for Writing Sounds Like a List. Record the score in the score box at the end of the test.

Score	What to Look for	Anchor Samples
4 Wow!	**The ideas are fully explained and supported.** The important ideas are well developed with concrete, sensory details.	Fernando, Kyoko and I were strolling back to our campsite after a long hike to the lake. Just as we reached our tent, Kyoko suddenly stopped in her tracks, and her eyes widened. "Did you hear that?" We then heard a rustling coming from our tent. Kyoko let out a high-pitched scream. "Shhh," Fernando whispered, as he crept towards our tent. Wild thoughts raced through my head: *What if it was a wild animal in the tent?* As Fernando approached the tent, he reached for a stick, "Come on out, little critter." I held my breath in anticipation. Just then, we heard a timid growl and a bear cub poked his head out. We knew we had to get to safety in case the mother bear was nearby. Fernando fumbled around in his pockets for his keys, "Get in the car!" he whispered. We calmly slid inside the car and watched as the cub finished feasting on our food. As soon as the cub left, we packed up our campsite. It was time to relocate.
3 Aaah.	**Most of the ideas are explained and supported.** Most of the important ideas are well developed with concrete, sensory details.	Fernando, Kyoko and I were strolling back to our campsite after a long hike to the lake. We got close to our tent, and Kyoko suddenly stopped in her tracks. Her eyes widened. She heard something. Fernando crept towards our tent. Wild thoughts raced through my head: *What if it was a wild animal in the tent?* As Fernando approached the tent, he reached for a stick, "Come on out, little critter." Just then, we heard a timid growl and a bear cub poked his head out. We knew we had to get to safety in case the mother bear was nearby. Fernando fumbled for his keys, "Get in the car!" he whispered. We calmly slid inside the car and watched as the cub finished feasting on our food. Finally, the cub left and we quickly packed up our campsite. It was time to relocate.
2 Hmmm.	**Some of the ideas are explained and supported.** Some of the important ideas are well developed with concrete, sensory details.	Fernando, Kyoko and I went camping. We chose a hidden campsite and put up our tent and unpacked our food. Then we went on a hike to the lake. When we returned to the campsite, we heard something in our tent. We heard a timid growl, and a bear cub poked his head out of our tent. Fernando fumbled for his keys. We went inside the car and watched as the cub finished feasting on all our food. Finally, the cub left, and we came out of the car. We quickly packed up our things and left. It was time to relocate.
1 Huh?	**The ideas are not explained and supported.** The ideas lack concrete, sensory details.	Fernando, Kyoko, and I went camping. We chose a hidden campsite. Then we put up our tent and unpacked our food. Then we went on a hike to the lake. When we got back, we heard something. Then a bear cub poked his head out of our tent. Fernando looked for his keys. We went inside the car. We watched as the cub finished feasting on our food. Finally, the cub left, and we quickly packed up our things. It was time to relocate.

Name _____

Date _____

Test: Writing Is Too Wordy

Directions: The paragraph below is too wordy. On a separate sheet of paper, rewrite the paragraph so that every word counts. Use the Solutions to help you revise.

A Quiet Place

I am going to write about how immediate surroundings affect people's lives. I feel it is important to say that noise affects concentration. I will talk about noise and concentration. I think that loud noises make it hard to concentrate. But I must say concentration is easy in a quiet place. The reason for this is because our brains can only concentrate on a certain amount of information at once. A good example of concentration problems is that I can't study when my brother's band rehearses in our garage. I want to tell you that they are loud! I have to go all the way to the library to concentrate and study.

Solutions:

- *Take Out Throwaway Writing:* Let your writing speak for itself.
- *Use Fewer Words:* Avoid extra words and repetition.

TEACHER USE ONLY Use the Writing Is Too Wordy rubric on page 50 to score the revision. Circle the score in the score box to the right.	**Rubric Score**	1	2	3	4
	Percent Score	25%	50%	75%	100%

Rubric and Anchor Samples: Writing Is Too Wordy

Use this rubric to score the test for Writing Is Too Wordy. Record the score in the score box at the end of the test.

Score	What to Look for	Anchor Samples
4 Wow!	**Words are thoughtfully and economically used.** • The writing introduces ideas efficiently. • The writing does not contain extra words and repetitions.	Surroundings affect people's lives. For example, noisy surroundings affect concentration. Loud noises make it hard to concentrate, whereas concentration is easy in quiet places. This is because our brains can only focus on a certain amount of information at once. I can't study, for example, when my brother's band rehearses in our garage. When they play, I escape the noise by going to the library to concentrate.
3 Aaah.	**Most words are thoughtfully and economically used.** • Most of the writing introduces ideas efficiently. • The writing contains very few extra words and repetitions.	Surroundings affect people's lives. The noise in one's surroundings particularly affects concentration. Loud noises make it hard to concentrate, whereas concentration is easy in quiet places. This is because our brains can only focus on a certain amount of information at once. A good example is that I can't study when my brother's band rehearses in our garage. They are so loud, I have to go to the library to concentrate.
2 Hmmm.	**Some words are thoughtfully and economically used.** • Some of the writing introduces ideas efficiently. • The writing contains several extra words and repetitions.	I am going to write about how surroundings affect people's lives. Most importantly noise particularly affects concentration. Loud noises make it hard to concentrate, whereas concentration is easy in a quiet place. This is because our brains can only concentrate on a certain amount of information at once. A good example of concentration problems is that I can't study when my brother's band rehearses in our garage. They are loud! I have to go to the library to concentrate.
1 Huh?	**The words are <u>not</u> thoughtfully and economically used.** • The writing does not introduce ideas efficiently. • The writing is cluttered with extra words and repetitions.	I am going to write about how surroundings affect people's lives. It is important to say that noise affects concentration. Loud noises make it hard to concentrate. But I must say concentration is easy in a quiet place. The reason is because our brains can only concentrate on a certain amount of information at once. A good example of concentration problems is that I can't study when my brother's band rehearses in our garage. They are loud! I have to go all the way to the library to concentrate and study.

Name _____

Date _____

Test: Sentences Are Boring

Directions: The sentences are boring in the paragraph below. On a separate sheet of paper, rewrite the paragraph so that the sentences are interesting. Use the Solutions to help you revise.

> ### A Lesson Learned
>
> When I was little, I was outside in the snow with my big sister. The snow on the metal fence in our back yard was about 4 inches high. I wanted to taste it. I did and my tongue got stuck to the fence. I could not move. I was so scared. I tried to scream, but couldn't. My sister ran inside and got a cup of warm water. She poured it over the fence and my tongue, and I was free. I learned to never put my tongue on metal in the snow.

Solutions:

- *Vary Your Sentences*
- *Spice Up Your Verbs*
- *Pepper Your Writing with Prepositional Phrases*
- *Move a Modifier*
- *Put in a Participle*
- *Add a Clause*
- *Add Absolutes*

TEACHER USE ONLY	Rubric Score	1	2	3	4
Use the Sentences Are Boring rubric on page 52 to score the revision. Circle the score in the score box to the right.	Percent Score	25%	50%	75%	100%

Rubric and Anchor Samples: Sentences Are Boring

Use this rubric to score the test for Sentences Are Boring. Record the score in the score box at the end of the test.

Score	What to Look for	Anchor Samples
4 Wow!	**The sentences are interesting and engaging.** • The sentences are varied in length and structure. • The writing engages the reader with details and vivid verbs.	Once, when I was a little girl, I was exploring in the snow with my big sister. To my delight, I discovered that the snow on our metal fence was at least 4 inches high. It looked so tempting, like a huge snow cone! I got up on my toes to stick out my tongue and taste it. My warm tongue suddenly felt like a popsicle with freezer burn! It was completely frozen! I tried to pull away, but my tongue was stuck to the fence. My arms began to flail as I stomped at the powdery snow beneath my feet. I tried to scream, but nothing would come out. My sister came to my rescue. She retrieved a cup of warm water from inside and poured it over the fence and my tongue. In a flash, I was free! If nothing else, I learned to never put my tongue on metal when it's snowy and cold outside.
3 Aaah.	**Most of the sentences are interesting and engaging.** • Most of the sentences are varied in length and structure. • Most of the writing engages the reader with details and vivid verbs.	When I was a little girl, I was playing in the snow with my big sister. I discovered that the snow on our metal fence was about 4 inches high. It looked so tempting, I wanted to taste it! I got up on my toes to taste it. My warm tongue suddenly felt like a popsicle that was completely frozen! My tongue was stuck to the fence. I tried to scream, but nothing would come out. I swung my arms about and stomped at the snow beneath my feet. My sister came to my rescue. She brought a cup of warm water from inside and poured it over the fence and my tongue. In a flash, I was free! I learned to never put my tongue on metal when it's snowy and cold outside.
2 Hmmm.	**Some of the sentences are interesting and engaging.** • Some of the sentences are varied in length and structure. • Some of the writing engages the reader with details and vivid verbs.	When I was little, I was outside in the snow with my big sister. I found that the snow on the metal fence in our backyard was about 4 inches high. It looked so tempting, I wanted to taste it! I put my warm tongue on the fence, and it became frozen! I was stuck and I tried to scream, but I couldn't. I was so scared. My sister ran inside and came back with a cup of warm water. She poured it over the fence and my tongue, and I was free! I learned to never put my tongue on something metal when it's snowy and cold.
1 Huh?	**The sentences are not interesting and engaging.** • The sentences lack variety. • The writing does not engage the reader.	When I was little, I was outside in the snow with my big sister. The snow on the metal fence in our backyard was about 4 inches high. I wanted to taste it. I did. My warm tongue got stuck to the fence. I could not move. I was so scared. I tried to scream, but nothing would come out. My sister ran inside and got a cup of warm water. She poured it over the fence and my tongue, and I was free. I learned to never put my tongue on metal in the snow.

Name _____

Date _____

Chapter Test: Form A

Directions: Choose one of the three prompts to write about. Write your composition on separate sheets of paper.

Look at the picture.

Write a short story or narrative composition about the picture. You may want to ask yourself: Who is this person? What book was he reading before he put his head down? Where is he? Is anyone else there? Why is he so tired?

Most people have goals in life. These goals may be big or small.

Write an expository composition about a goal that you once had or still have. Explain what the goal was, why it was important, and how it was or was not achieved.

Your school board will be voting on whether the school day should begin and end an hour later so that students are more awake for their classes.

Is this a good idea? Write a persuasive composition that will be read by the school board in which you convince them to vote with your opinion on this issue.

TEACHER USE ONLY

Use the Good Writing Traits rubric on page 11a to score the composition for each trait. Circle the scores in the score box to the right. For the overall percent score, divide the total number of points earned by 20.

Focus and Unity	1	2	3	4
Organization	1	2	3	4
Idea Development	1	2	3	4
Voice and Style	1	2	3	4
Written Conventions	1	2	3	4
Overall Percent	____ Points / 20 = ____ %			

Name _____

Date _____

Chapter Test: Form B

Directions: Choose one of the three prompts to write about. Write your composition on separate sheets of paper.

Prompt 1

Look at the picture.

Write a short story or narrative composition about the picture. You may want to ask yourself: Who are these people? What does the music sound like? Where are they? Is anyone else there? Why is the girl playing a trumpet?

Prompt 2

Many people say that we can learn from our elders.

Write an expository composition about a time when you learned from an older person. Explain who the older person was, what you learned, and how you learned it.

Prompt 3

Your school board will be voting on whether to eliminate music classes from your school in order to allow more time for reading, writing, and math.

Is this a good idea? Write a persuasive composition that will be read by the school board in which you convince them to vote with your position on this issue.

TEACHER USE ONLY

Use the Good Writing Traits rubric on page 11a to score the composition for each trait. Circle the scores in the score box to the right. For the overall percent score, divide the total number of points earned by 20.

Focus and Unity	1	2	3	4
Organization	1	2	3	4
Idea Development	1	2	3	4
Voice and Style	1	2	3	4
Written Conventions	1	2	3	4
Overall Percent	____ Points / 20 = ____ %			

Writing Clinic

STUDENT NAME	Test: Writing Wanders	Test: Can't Write Enough	Test: Writing Is Not Connected	Test: Writing Is Too Vague	Test: Writing Sounds Like A List	Test: Writing Is Too Wordy	Test: Sentences Are Boring	Chapter Test A	Chapter Test B
	Date	Date	Date	Date	Date	Date	Date	Date	Date

Reviewer _____

Writer _____

Date _____

Peer-Review: Reflective Essay

Directions: Read your partner's essay. For questions 1–7, circle the number that matches your opinion of the essay.

Does the essay . . .	Needs Improvement	Well Done
❶ begin with an interesting detail?	1	2
❷ introduce one memory or moment as the topic?	1	2
❸ contain clear descriptions and sensory details?	1	2
❹ maintain the writer's unique voice throughout?	1	2
❺ use effective transitions that guide the reader?	1	2
❻ end with a memorable conclusion that includes a reflection?	1	2
❼ use standard written conventions?	1	2

Directions: Answer questions 8 and 9. If you need more room, use the back of the page.

8. What do you like best about your partner's essay? _____

_____

_____

_____

9. How could your partner improve the essay? _____

_____

_____

_____

Reviewer _____

Writer _____

Date _____

Peer-Review: Letter of Problem Solving

Directions: Read your partner's letter. For questions 1–6, circle the number that matches your opinion of the letter.

Does the letter . . .	Needs Improvement	Well Done
1 look professional and is it correctly formatted?	1	2
2 clearly state the problem?	1	2
3 contain facts and details about the problem?	1	2
4 propose a clear solution?	1	2
5 use a polite, yet firm tone?	1	2
6 use standard written conventions?	1	2

Directions: Answer questions 7 and 8. If you need more room, use the back of the page.

7. What do you like best about your partner's letter? _____

_____

_____

_____

_____

8. How could your partner improve the letter? _____

_____

_____

_____

_____

Reviewer _____

Writer _____

Date _____

Peer-Review: Short, Short Story

Directions: Read your partner's story. For questions 1–7, circle the number that matches your opinion of the story.

Does the story . . .	Needs Improvement	Well Done
1 begin with a brief description of the setting and quickly move to the plot?	1	2
2 follow a series of events with one clear turning point?	1	2
3 contain details and dialogue that develop the characters?	1	2
4 have a clear point of view and voice that is appropriate to the purpose and audience?	1	2
5 use a tone that creates one emotional effect?	1	2
6 have a short and sweet ending?	1	2
7 use standard written conventions?	1	2

Directions: Answer questions 8 and 9. If you need more room, use the back of the page.

8. What do you like best about your partner's story? _____

_____

_____

_____

9. How could your partner improve the story? _____

_____

_____

_____

Reviewer _____

Writer _____

Date _____

Peer-Review: Persuasive Essay

Directions: Read your partner's essay. For questions 1–8, circle the number that matches your opinion of the essay.

Does the essay . . .	Needs Improvement	Well Done
1 present background information and a thesis statement in the introduction?	1	2
2 follow a well-organized format and present the most important ideas first?	1	2
3 build a case that appeals both to logic and emotions?	1	2
4 provide evidence that is supported by personal experience, expert explanations, facts, and/or statistics?	1	2
5 address reader objections in a calm tone?	1	2
6 use a voice and style that are appropriate to the purpose and audience?	1	2
7 end with a strong conclusion and a call to action?	1	2
8 use standard written conventions?	1	2

Directions: Answer questions 9 and 10. If you need more room, use the back of the page.

9. What do you like best about your partner's essay? _____

_____

_____

_____

10. How could your partner improve the essay? _____

_____

_____

_____

Reviewer _____

Writer _____

Date _____

Peer-Review: Literary Critique

Directions: Read your partner's critique. For questions 1–6, circle the number that matches your opinion of the critique.

Does the literary critique . . .	Needs Improvement	Well Done
❶ include the title and author of the work in the introduction?	1	2
❷ hook the readers with an interesting detail and state the critic's overall opinion in the introduction?	1	2
❸ support main ideas and opinions with details and quotations from the work?	1	2
❹ present a mostly balanced, objective view?	1	2
❺ restate the critic's overall opinion and a personal reflection in the conclusion?	1	2
❻ use standard written conventions?	1	2

Directions: Answer questions 7 and 8. If you need more room, use the back of the page.

7. What do you like best about your partner's critique? _____

_____

_____

_____

8. How could your partner improve the critique? _____

_____

_____

_____

_____

Reviewer _____

Writer _____

Date _____

Peer-Review: Résumé

Directions: Read your partner's résumé. For questions 1–6, circle the number that matches your opinion of the résumé.

Does the résumé . . .	Needs Improvement	Well Done
❶ look serious and professional?	1	2
❷ clearly display contact information, an objective, and a profile?	1	2
❸ follow a well-organized format with headings that are easy to read?	1	2
❹ emphasize skills and accomplishments related to the desired job?	1	2
❺ make use of precise language and active verbs to describe job duties?	1	2
❻ use standard written conventions?	1	2

Directions: Answer questions 7 and 8. If you need more room, use the back of the page.

7. What do you like best about your partner's résumé? _____

_____

_____

_____

_____

8. How could your partner improve the résumé? _____

_____

_____

_____

_____

Reviewer _____

Writer _____

Date _____

Peer-Review: News Article

Directions: Read your partner's news article. For questions 1–8, circle the number that matches your opinion of the article.

Does the article . . .	Needs Improvement	Well Done
1 have a headline that gets the reader's attention and sums up the topic or event?	1	2
2 begin with a lead paragraph that provides essential facts about the topic or event?	1	2
3 start with the most important information first?	1	2
4 answer the 5 Ws: *Who, What, When, Where,* and *Why*?	1	2
5 provide facts and background information that show why the story matters?	1	2
6 maintain an objective tone throughout?	1	2
7 end with information that is relevant, but not essential?	1	2
8 use standard written conventions?	1	2

Directions: Answer questions 9 and 10. If you need more room, use the back of the page.

9. What do you like best about your partner's article? _____

_____

_____

_____

10. How could your partner improve the article? _____

_____

_____

_____

Reviewer _____

Writer _____

Date _____

Peer-Review: Poem in Free Verse

Directions: Read your partner's poem. For questions 1–5, circle the number that matches your opinion of the poem.

Does the poem . . .	Needs Improvement	Well Done
1 grab and maintain the reader's or listener's attention?	1	2
2 have a good rhythm and appealing sounds?	1	2
3 focus on a specific idea or topic?	1	2
4 contain details, imagery, and vivid words that give it life?	1	2
5 produce an emotional effect?	1	2

Directions: Answer questions 6 and 7. If you need more room, use the back of the page.

6. What do you like best about your partner's poem? _____

_____

_____

_____

7. How could your partner improve the poem? _____

_____

_____

_____

Name _____

Date _____

Chapter Test: Form A

Directions: Write a composition, using a photograph from Step 1, a role from Step 2, and a form from Step 3. Write your composition on separate sheets of paper.

Step 1. Choose a photograph to write about. Put a ✔ next to your photo.

GO ON

Name _____

Date _____

Step 2. Choose a role for your composition. Put a ✓ next to your role.

> **Check One:**
>
> ❏ a family member   ❏ a citizen   ❏ an employee
>
> ❏ a consumer   ❏ a critic   ❏ an entertainer

Step 3. Choose a form for your composition. Put a ✓ next to your form.

> **Check One:**
>
> ❏ analysis of an issue   ❏ essay   ❏ parody
>
> ❏ autobiography   ❏ letter   ❏ review
>
> ❏ biography   ❏ literary critique   ❏ speech
>
> ❏ description   ❏ literary response   ❏ story
>
> ❏ editorial   ❏ memoir   ❏ other _____

Step 4. Write a composition about the photograph in the role and form you chose. Write it on separate sheets of paper.

TEACHER USE ONLY

Use the Good Writing Traits rubric (p. 11a–b) to score each trait. Circle the scores in the score box to the right. For the overall percent score, divide the total number of points earned by 20.

Focus and Unity	1	2	3	4
Organization	1	2	3	4
Idea Development	1	2	3	4
Voice and Style	1	2	3	4
Written Conventions	1	2	3	4
Overall Percent	_____ Points / 20 = _____ %			

Name _____

Date _____

Chapter Test: Form B

Directions: Write a composition, using a photograph from Step 1, a role from Step 2, and a form from Step 3. Write your composition on separate sheets of paper.

Step 1. Choose a photograph to write about. Put a ✔ next to your photo.

GO ON ➡

Name _____

Date _____

Step 2. Choose a role for your composition. Put a ✔ next to your role.

> **Check One:**
>
> ☐ a family member ☐ a citizen ☐ an employee
>
> ☐ a consumer ☐ a critic ☐ an entertainer

Step 3. Choose a form for your composition. Put a ✔ next to your form.

> **Check One:**
>
> ☐ analysis of an issue ☐ essay ☐ parody
>
> ☐ autobiography ☐ letter ☐ review
>
> ☐ biography ☐ literary critique ☐ speech
>
> ☐ description ☐ literary response ☐ story
>
> ☐ editorial ☐ memoir ☐ other _____

Step 4. Write a composition about the photograph in the role and form you chose. Write it on separate sheets of paper.

TEACHER USE ONLY				
Use the Good Writing Traits rubric (p. 11a–b) to score each trait. Circle the scores in the score box to the right. For the overall percent score, divide the total number of points earned by 20.				

Focus and Unity	1	2	3	4
Organization	1	2	3	4
Idea Development	1	2	3	4
Voice and Style	1	2	3	4
Written Conventions	1	2	3	4
Overall Percent	____ Points / 20 = ____ %			

Class Record Form

Test Results

STUDENT NAME	OVERALL SCORE	Focus & Unity	Organization	Development of Ideas	Voice & Style	Written Conventions

Name _____

Date _____

Digging Up the Facts Test

Directions: Answer questions 1–6 to help you plan a research report.

A. Research Topic

1. The five topics below are very broad. Put a ✔ next to the topic you will narrow.

Broad Topics: ☐ Music ☐ Technology ☐ Sports ☐ Art ☐ History

2. Narrow your topic by writing in the inverted triangle. Make the topic narrow enough to write a research report about it.

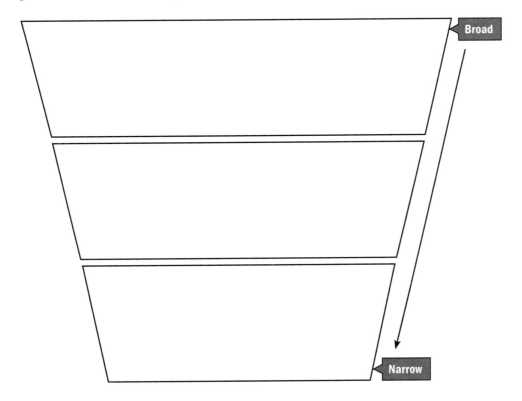

Name _____

Date _____

B. Research Questions

3. Now write four research questions about your topic. Make them as specific as possible.

_____

_____

_____

_____

_____

_____

_____

_____

C. Research Sources

4. List four sources from which you could gather information about your topic. Include one direct-observation source, one expert source, and two published sources in your answer.

_____

_____

_____

_____

_____

_____

_____

_____

Name _____ ____%

Date _____

D. Plagiarism

5. What is plagiarism?

_____

_____

_____

_____

_____

_____

6. List two or more possible consequences of plagiarism.

_____

_____

_____

_____

_____

_____

_____

_____

DONE!

TEACHER USE ONLY

Use the Digging Up the Facts rubric on page 68 to score A–D.
Circle the scores in the score box to the right. For the overall
percent score, divide the total number of points earned by 16.

A. Research Topic	1	2	3	4
B. Research Questions	1	2	3	4
C. Research Sources	1	2	3	4
D. Plagiarism	1	2	3	4
Overall Percent	___ Points / 16 = ___ %			

Digging Up the Facts Rubric

Use this rubric to score the Digging Up the Facts Test. Record the scores in the score box at the end of the test.

Score	A. Research Topic	B. Research Questions	C. Research Sources	D. Plagiarism
4	The topic is narrow enough for a research report.	Writes 4 specific research questions about the topic.	Lists 4 sources, including 1 direct-observation, 1 expert, and 2 published sources.	Fully defines plagiarism and explains 2 or more possible consequences.
3	The topic is narrowed, but it remains somewhat broad for a research report.	Writes 3 specific research questions about the topic.	Lists 3 sources, no more than 2 of which are published sources.	Adequately defines plagiarism and explains 1 possible consequence.
2	The topic is narrowed slightly, but it is too broad for a research report.	Writes 2 specific research questions about the topic.	Lists 2 sources.	Defines plagiarism or explains a possible consequence.
1	A broad topic is chosen, but it is not narrowed.	Writes 1 specific research question about the topic.	Lists 1 source.	Minimally defines plagiarism or states a possible consequence.

Name _____

Date _____

Making Sense of Your Notes Test

Directions: Use the list of notes below to complete steps A–D.

Notes for a Research Report

1. Modern construction materials allowed parks to make taller and faster roller coasters.
2. The first roller coasters were more like log flumes.
3. Six-Flags amusement park built the Run-Away Mine Train, one of the earliest roller coasters.
4. In 2003, Cedar Point amusement park built the Top Thrill Dragster roller coaster.
5. The Top Thrill Dragster roller coaster is 420 feet tall.
6. A log flume pulls people up to the top of one big hill and lets them roll down the hill into a splash of water.
7. The Run-Away Mine Train was made of wood.
8. Metal is stronger than wood, so roller coasters could be taller.
9. The Run-Away Mine Train was only 60 feet tall.
10. The Top Thrill Dragster roller coaster travels 120 miles per hour.
11. Fiberglass is strong and light, so roller coasters could move faster.
12. The Run-Away Mine Train traveled only 25 miles per hour.

69a

Name _____

Date _____

A. Organize Notes

Organize the 12 notes on the previous page under the following two headings.

Early Roller Coasters

_____

_____

_____

_____

_____

_____

Modern Roller Coasters

_____

_____

_____

_____

_____

_____

B. Synthesize Notes

Write two paragraphs using the notes above. If you need more room, use the back of the paper.

_____

_____

_____

_____

_____

_____

GO ON →

Name _____

Date _____

C. Main Outline

Write a title for the report about roller coasters. List the main topics beside the Roman numerals below.

Title _____

I. _____

II. _____

III. _____

IV. _____

D. Subtopics

Copy your main topics beside the Roman numerals below. Now fill in subtopics and supporting details under each main topic of your outline.

I. _____

_____

II. _____

_____

_____

III. _____

_____

_____

IV. _____

_____

DONE!

TEACHER USE ONLY

Use the Making Sense of Your Notes rubric on page 70 to score A–D. Circle the scores in the score box to the right. For the overall percent score, divide the total number of points earned by 16.

A. Organize Notes	1	2	3	4
B. Synthesize Notes	1	2	3	4
C. Main Outline	1	2	3	4
D. Subtopics	1	2	3	4
Overall Percent	____ Points / 16 = ____ %			

Making Sense of Your Notes Rubric

Use this rubric to score the Making Sense of Your Notes Test. Record the scores in the score box at the end of the test.

Score	A. Organize Notes	B. Synthesize Notes	C. Main Outline	D. Subtopics
4	Organizes all 12 notes under the appropriate headings.	Effectively pulls all notes together into two paragraphs.	Writes an appropriate title and main topics, such as: *Roller Coasters, Then and Now* *I. Introduction* *II. Early Coasters* *III. Modern Coasters* *IV. Conclusion*	Writes appropriate subtopics under 4 of the main topics.
3	Organizes most of the 12 notes under the appropriate headings.	Pulls most notes together into two paragraphs.	Writes an appropriate title and 3 appropriate main topics.	Writes appropriate subtopics under 3 of the main topics.
2	Organizes some of the 12 notes under the appropriate headings.	Pulls some notes together into 1 or 2 paragraphs.	Writes an appropriate title and 2 appropriate main topics.	Writes appropriate subtopics under 2 of the main topics.
1	Organizes a few of the 12 notes under the appropriate headings.	Lists notes without much, if any, synthesis.	Writes an appropriate title or 1 appropriate main topic.	Writes appropriate subtopic(s) under 1 of the main topics.

Name _____

Date _____

Packaging Your Ideas Test

Directions: Answer questions 1–4.

1. Read the outline below. Write the introduction for the research report on the next page.

Outline for a Research Report

Title: "Leonardo da Vinci, Renaissance Man"

I. Introduction

    A. The Renaissance era was a time when people were curious about the world and interested in everything.

    B. The term Renaissance means "rebirth."

    C. Leonardo da Vinci lived from 1452–1519, during the Renaissance era.

    D. Leonardo da Vinci had many interests, more than most people know.

II. Leonardo the Painter

    A. Most famous as a painter

    B. Painted *The Mona Lisa*

    C. Painted *The Last Supper*

III. Leonardo the Scientist

    A. Studied math

    B. Studied plants and animals

    C. Studied waves and the wind

IV. Leonardo the Inventor

    A. Invented an army tank

    B. Invented a small submarine

    C. Invented a parachute

V. Conclusion

    A. Today, calling someone a Renaissance person means that the person has many interests.

    B. Leonardo was one of the first Renaissance Men, interested in everything.

Name _____

Date _____

Write the introduction to the report "Leonardo da Vinci, Renaissance Man" here:

_____

_____

_____

_____

_____

_____

_____

_____

_____

_____

_____

_____

2. Explain how and why you should cite sources in a research report.

_____

_____

_____

_____

_____

_____

_____

_____

GO ON

Packaging Your Ideas Test, continued

3. Name two ways you can create a multimedia report.
    Give an example of each way.

    _____

    _____

    _____

    _____

    _____

    _____

    _____

    _____

4. Name two things you should do to prepare for an oral report.
    Explain why doing these things are important.

    _____

    _____

    _____

    _____

    _____

    _____

    _____

    _____

DONE!

TEACHER USE ONLY

Use the Packaging Your Ideas rubric on page 72 to score questions
1–4. Circle the scores in the score box to the right. For the overall
percent score, divide the total number of points earned by 16.

	1	2	3	4
Question 1	1	2	3	4
Question 2	1	2	3	4
Question 3	1	2	3	4
Question 4	1	2	3	4
Overall Percent	____ Points / 16 = ____ %			

Packaging Your Ideas Rubric

Use this rubric to score the Packaging Your Ideas Test. Record the scores in the score box at the end of the test.

Score	Question 1	Question 2	Question 3	Question 4
4	Introduction is engaging and introduces the main ideas of subsequent paragraphs.	Fully explains how and why one should cite sources in a research report.	Names 2 ways to create a multimedia report and gives an example for each.	Names 2 things to do to prepare for an oral report and explains why they are important.
3	Introduction introduces the main ideas of most subsequent paragraphs.	Adequately explains how and why one should cite sources in a research report.	Names 2 ways to create a multimedia report and gives an example for one way.	Names 2 things to do to prepare for an oral report and explains why one is important.
2	Introduction states some of the main topic information.	Fully explains how or why one should cite sources in a research report, or partially explains both.	Names 2 ways to create a multimedia report. No examples. OR Names one way and gives an example.	Names 2 things to do to prepare for an oral report. No explanation OR Names and explains one.
1	Introduction contains any piece of information from the outline.	Minimally explains how or why one should cite sources in a research report.	Names 1 way to create a multimedia report.	Names 1 thing to do to prepare for an oral report.

Name _____

Date _____

Chapter Test: Form A

Directions: For question **1**, order the stages of the writing process from **1** to **5** on the lines below.

1. Stages of the research process:

___ Investigate Sources

___ Synthesize Ideas

___ Take Notes

___ Write Research Questions

___ Develop an Outline

Directions: For questions **2–10**, mark your answer as shown in the sample.

Sample

If a Web address ends in .biz, the site is maintained by a

Ⓐ business.

Ⓑ professional organization.

Ⓒ school, college, or university.

Ⓓ federal government organization.

2. Interviewing a doctor about diabetes is an example of using which type of source?

Ⓐ original

Ⓑ expert

Ⓒ print

Ⓓ Web

3. When you put what an author has written in your own words, you are

Ⓕ organizing.

Ⓖ summarizing.

Ⓗ paraphrasing.

Ⓙ synthesizing.

4. If a Web address ends in .org, the site is maintained by a

Ⓐ state government.

Ⓑ professional organization.

Ⓒ business or individual.

Ⓓ school, college, or university.

5. Which is the best way to decide if a book has the information you need?

Ⓕ read the table of contents

Ⓖ ask the librarian

Ⓗ read the entire book

Ⓙ ask people in a chat room

6. How should you list sources alphabetically in the works-cited page of your report?

Ⓐ by title

Ⓑ by type of source

Ⓒ by author's first name

Ⓓ by author's last name

GO ON ➡

7. Which statement about plagiarism is true?

Ⓕ It's easy to plagiarize without getting caught.

Ⓖ Plagiarism is a great way to beat the system.

Ⓗ Sloppy notes can lead to accidental plagiarism.

Ⓙ It's not plagiarism if you change the author's wording a little bit.

8. Read the FATP chart.

Form: research report

Audience: students, faculty, and parents

Topic: pros and cons of school uniforms

Purpose: to inform

Which type of essay would be most appropriate for the topic and purpose?

Ⓐ persuasive

Ⓑ descriptive

Ⓒ cause and effect

Ⓓ compare and contrast

9. You might use a checklist or journal when

Ⓕ planning your oral report.

Ⓖ practicing your oral report.

Ⓗ delivering your oral report.

Ⓙ reflecting on your oral report.

10. A computer file of information related to a particular subject is

Ⓐ a search engine.

Ⓑ a trade journal.

Ⓒ an online database.

Ⓓ an online catalogue.

DONE!

Number Correct	x 10 =	Percent Score
	x 10 =	_____ %

Name _____

Date _____

Chapter Test: Form B

Directions: For question **1**, order the stages of the writing process from **1** to **5** on the lines below.

1. Stages of the research process:

___ Take Notes

___ Investigate Sources

___ Develop an Outline

___ Write Research Questions

___ Synthesize Ideas

Directions: For questions **2–10**, mark your answer as shown in the sample.

Sample

If a Web address ends in .biz, the site is maintained by a

Ⓐ business.

Ⓑ professional organization.

Ⓒ school, college, or university.

Ⓓ federal government organization.

2. Going to a museum to research a painting is an example of using which type of source?

Ⓐ original

Ⓑ expert

Ⓒ print

Ⓓ Web

3. If a Web address ends in .edu, the site is maintained by a

Ⓕ state government.

Ⓖ professional organization.

Ⓗ business or individual.

Ⓙ school, college, or university.

4. When you pull ideas together from different sources, you are

Ⓐ organizing.

Ⓑ summarizing.

Ⓒ paraphrasing.

Ⓓ synthesizing.

5. In the works-cited page of your report, you should list sources alphabetically by

Ⓕ title.

Ⓖ type of source.

Ⓗ author's last name.

Ⓙ author's first name.

6. What should you **never** do while searching the Web?

Ⓐ subscribe to an online publication

Ⓑ give out personal information in chat rooms

Ⓒ click the back button on your Web browser

Ⓓ post comments on a blog or discussion board

Name _____

Date _____

7. Read the FATP chart.

Form: research report

Audience: students, faculty, and parents

Topic: impact of fishing on the fish population

Purpose: to inform

Which type of essay would be most appropriate for the topic and purpose?

Ⓕ persuasive

Ⓖ descriptive

Ⓗ cause and effect

Ⓙ compare and contrast

8. A computer program capable of scanning the entire World Wide Web is

Ⓐ a search engine.

Ⓑ a trade journal.

Ⓒ an online database.

Ⓓ an online catalogue.

9. You might give your oral report in front of a mirror when

Ⓕ planning it.

Ⓖ practicing it.

Ⓗ delivering it.

Ⓙ reflecting on it.

10. Which statement about plagiarism is true?

Ⓐ It's easy to plagiarize without getting caught.

Ⓑ Plagiarism is a great way to beat the system.

Ⓒ Listing sources on your note cards is a waste of time.

Ⓓ Any time you use an author's words or ideas, you must cite the source.

DONE!

Number Correct	x 10 =	Percent Score
_____	x 10 =	_____ %

74b

Chapter 5

Research and Writing

STUDENT NAME	Test: Digging Up the Facts		Test: Making Sense of Your Notes		Test: Packaging Your Ideas		Chapter Test A		Chapter Test B	
	Date		Date		Date		Date		Date	

Research and Writing

STUDENT NAME	Test: Digging Up the Facts	Test: Making Sense of Your Notes	Test: Packaging Your Ideas	Chapter Test A	Chapter Test B
	Date _____	Date _____	Date _____	Date _____	Date _____

Tracking Forms

Affective Measures

The Writing Process

Written Composition

The Research Process

Answer Keys

Directions: Write student names in the row to the right. Record administration dates in the appropriate cell.

NAMES

Ch.1: Prewriting									
Ch.1: Drafting									
Ch.1: Revising									
Ch.1: Editing & Proofreading									
Ch.1: Publishing									
Ch.1: Test Form A									
Ch.1: Test Form B									
Ch. 2: Focus & Unity									
Ch. 2: Organization									
Ch. 2: Development of Ideas									
Ch. 2: Voice & Style									
Ch. 2: Written Conventions									
Ch. 2: Test Form A									
Ch. 2: Test Form B									
Ch. 3: Writing Wanders									
Ch. 3: Can't Write Enough									
Ch. 3: Writing Is Not Connected									
Ch. 3: Writing Is Too Vague									
Ch. 3: Writing Sounds Like a List									
Ch. 3: Writing Is Too Wordy									
Ch. 3: Sentences Are Boring									
Ch. 3: Test Form A									
Ch. 3: Test Form B									
Ch. 4: Writing as a Family Member									
Ch. 4: Writing as a Consumer									
Ch. 4: Writing as an Entertainer									
Ch. 4: Writing as a Citizen									
Ch. 4: Writing as a Critic									
Ch. 4: Writing as an Employee									
Ch. 4: Writing as a Reporter									
Ch. 4: Writing as a Poet									
Ch. 4: Test Form A									
Ch. 4: Test Form B									
Ch. 5: Digging Up the Facts									
Ch. 5: Making Sense of Your Notes									
Ch. 5: Packaging Your Ideas									
Ch. 5: Test Form A									
Ch. 5: Test Form B									
Benchmark Test: Expository									
Benchmark Test: Persuasive									
Benchmark Test: Literary Analysis									
Benchmark Test: Narrative									
Benchmark Test: Reflective									

Good Writing Traits

Assignment ——————— Date ——————— Period ———————

Directions: Use the **Good Writing Traits Rubric** on page 11a to score students' written compositions. Then plot the scores on the Rubric below by writing each student's initials in the appropriate cell. Identify the trait(s) with which the most students need practice. Use Chapter 2 of the Good Writer's Guide to focus instruction on a writing trait.

Scale	Focus & Unity	Organization	Development of Ideas	Voice & Style	Written Conventions
4					
3					
2					
1					

Tools: Additional Assessments

Class Tally for Self-Assessments

Directions: Use this generic chart to tally class results for self-assessments. Write the questions in the left column of the chart. Then plot student responses by writing each student's initials in the cell with the corresponding rating.

Self-Assessment _____ Date _____ Period _____

Questions	1	2	3	4

Self-Assessment: Who Am I as a Writer?

Directions: This survey will help you discover who you are as a writer. Answer parts A-D.

A. What interests me?

Directions: Put a ✔ next to all the topics that interest you. If you do not see your interests, add them to the list.

My Self
- ❑ hopes
- ❑ dreams
- ❑ strengths
- ❑ personality
- ❑ other: _____

My Family
- ❑ parents
- ❑ brothers/sisters
- ❑ memories
- ❑ vacations
- ❑ other: _____

My Friends
- ❑ best friends
- ❑ disagreements
- ❑ helpful friends
- ❑ spending time together
- ❑ other: _____

My Community
- ❑ the neighborhood
- ❑ neighborhood people
- ❑ doing things together
- ❑ things to improve
- ❑ other: _____

My Country
- ❑ history
- ❑ government
- ❑ laws
- ❑ states/cities/towns
- ❑ other: _____

My World
- ❑ the environment
- ❑ travel/exploration
- ❑ history
- ❑ countries/cultures
- ❑ other: _____

My Beliefs
- ❑ values
- ❑ religion
- ❑ philosophy
- ❑ holidays
- ❑ other: _____

My Feelings
- ❑ fear
- ❑ excitement
- ❑ love
- ❑ wonder
- ❑ other: _____

My Hobbies
- ❑ games/sports
- ❑ cars
- ❑ music/dance
- ❑ cooking
- ❑ other: _____

My School
- ❑ teachers
- ❑ activities
- ❑ classmates
- ❑ classes
- ❑ other: _____

My Future
- ❑ job/college
- ❑ relationships
- ❑ apartment/house
- ❑ children
- ❑ other: _____

Add to the List
_____
_____
_____
_____
_____

Now list 3 topics that most interest you. Write why you are interested in them.

1. _____ Why? _____

2. _____ Why? _____

3. _____ Why? _____

Name _____

Date _____

B. For whom do I write?

Directions: Read the list of people you may write for. Circle the number that shows how often you write for these people.

How often do you write for . . .	Never	Rarely	Sometimes	Often
❶ yourself?	1	2	3	4
❷ friends?	1	2	3	4
❸ family?	1	2	3	4
❹ teachers?	1	2	3	4
❺ employers?	1	2	3	4
❻ strangers?	1	2	3	4
❼ someone else: _____?	1	2	3	4

For whom do you most like to write? _____

C. Why do I write?

Directions: Read the list of reasons you may write. Circle the number that shows how often you write for these reasons.

How often do you write to . . .	Never	Rarely	Sometimes	Often
❶ teach people something?	1	2	3	4
❷ explain something to people?	1	2	3	4
❸ entertain people?	1	2	3	4
❹ make people feel emotion?	1	2	3	4
❺ persuade people to believe something?	1	2	3	4
❻ persuade people to do something?	1	2	3	4
❼ express how you feel?	1	2	3	4
❽ express what you think?	1	2	3	4
❾ do something else: _____?	1	2	3	4

For what reason do you most like to write? _____

Who Am I as a Writer?, continued

D. What do I write?

Directions: Put a ✔ next to all the writing forms that you use, and answer the questions.

❏ I write lists.
What types of lists do you write? _____

_____

❏ I write emails or letters.
What types of emails or letters do you write? _____

_____

❏ I write directions.
What types of directions do you write? _____

_____

❏ I write song or rap lyrics.
What types of lyrics do you write? _____

_____

❏ I write diary or journal entries.
What types of diary or journal entries do you write? _____

_____

❏ I write notes to myself.
What types of notes do you write? _____

_____

❏ I write a job application or resume.
What types of applications or resumes do you write? _____

_____

❏ I write poetry.
What types of poetry do you write? _____

_____

❏ I write stories.
What types of stories do you write? _____

_____

❏ I write screenplays.
What types of screenplays do you write? _____

_____

❏ I write reviews.
What types of reviews do you write? _____

_____

❏ I write speeches.
What types of speeches do you write? _____

_____

❏ I write essays.
What types of essays do you write? _____

_____

❏ I write reports.
What types of reports do you write? _____

_____

❏ I write articles.
What types of articles do you write? _____

_____

❏ I write cartoons, comic strips, or graphic novels.
What types of cartoons, comic strips, or graphic novels do you write? _____

_____

In which form do you most like to write? _____

Name _____

Date _____

Self-Assessment: How Do I Feel about Writing?

Directions: Read the sentences about writing. Circle the numbers that show how much you agree or disagree with each sentence.

	Strongly Disagree	Disagree	Agree	Strongly Agree
❶ I like to write.	1	2	3	4
❷ I think I am a good writer.	1	2	3	4
❸ My teachers think that my writing is good.	1	2	3	4
❹ I write better about things that interest me.	1	2	3	4
❺ I like to share my writing with others.	1	2	3	4
❻ I like to help other people with their writing.	1	2	3	4
❼ Writing is easy for me.	1	2	3	4
❽ My writing is better than it used to be.	1	2	3	4
❾ I am trying to improve my writing.	1	2	3	4
❿ It is important to know how to write.	1	2	3	4

Name _____

Date _____

Self-Assessment: How Am I Doing with the Writing Process?

Directions: For many people, some stages of the writing process are easier to do than others. Read the list of things people do when they write. Circle the numbers that show how hard or how easy you think each stage is.

	Hard	Somewhat Hard	Somewhat Easy	Easy
1 Deciding what I want to write about	1	2	3	4
2 Organizing my thoughts for writing	1	2	3	4
3 Thinking of enough things to say in my writing	1	2	3	4
4 Getting feedback on my writing from others	1	2	3	4
5 Changing my writing to make it better	1	2	3	4
6 Correcting little mistakes in my writing	1	2	3	4
7 Deciding when my writing is finished	1	2	3	4
8 Sharing my writing with others	1	2	3	4

Directions: Answer questions 9 and 10. If you need more room, use the back of the page.

9. Which stage of the writing process do you think is the easiest? Explain why. _____

_____

_____

10. Which stage of the writing process do you think is the hardest? Explain why. _____

_____

_____

Name _____

Date _____

Writing Process Reflection Form

Directions: Reflect on the process you used to write your composition titled _____.

Prewriting

1. What did you do that helped you brainstorm and plan your composition? _____
   _____

2. What will you do differently when you brainstorm and plan your next composition? _____
   _____

Drafting

3. What did you do that helped you draft your composition? _____
   _____

4. What will you do differently when you draft your next composition? _____
   _____

Revising

5. What did you do that helped you revise your composition? _____
   _____

6. What will you do differently when you revise your next composition? _____
   _____

Editing and Proofreading

7. What did you do that helped you edit your composition? _____
   _____

8. What will you do differently when you edit your next composition? _____
   _____

Publishing

9. What did you do that helped you publish your composition? _____
   _____

10. What will you do differently when you publish your next composition? _____
    _____

Name _____

Date _____

Self-Assessment: Prewriting

Directions: Read the questions about what people do when prewriting their compositions. Circle the numbers that show how often you do these things.

How often do you . . .	Never	Rarely	Sometimes	Often
1 ask yourself questions to help you think of topics to write about?	1	2	3	4
2 save extra ideas to write about later?	1	2	3	4
3 narrow your topic before you write?	1	2	3	4
4 think about your audience before you write?	1	2	3	4
5 choose your tone based on your audience?	1	2	3	4
6 write for a specific purpose?	1	2	3	4
7 choose a form in which to write?	1	2	3	4
8 organize your ideas before you write?	1	2	3	4

Directions: Answer questions 9–12. If you need more room, use the back of the page.

9. Do you do other things before you start to write? Describe what you do. _____

_____

10. How do you decide what to write about?_____

_____

11. What topics would you like to write about?_____

_____

12. Do you write on paper, on a computer, or on both at different times? Describe what you do. _____

_____

Name _____

Date _____

Self-Assessment: Drafting

Directions: Read the questions about what people do when drafting their compositions. Circle the numbers that show how often you do these things.

How often do you . . .	Never	Rarely	Sometimes	Often
1 use your prewriting ideas and information (brainstorming, FATP chart)?	1	2	3	4
2 add information that was not included in your prewriting?	1	2	3	4
3 write multiple paragraphs with multiple sentences in your first draft?	1	2	3	4
4 use your graphic organizer to create an engaging introduction, a memorable conclusion, and a middle that leads from your introduction to your conclusion?	1	2	3	4

Directions: Answer questions 5–8. If you need more room, use the back of the page.

5. How do you start writing your first draft? _____

_____

6. Do you write for long periods of time or a little bit at a time? _____

_____

7. How many drafts do you usually write before you finish writing something? _____

_____

8. What is the most number of drafts that you have written for one paper? _____

_____

Name _____

Date _____

Self-Assessment: Revising

Directions: Read the questions about what people do when revising their compositions. Circle the numbers that show how often you do these things.

How often do you . . .	Never	Rarely	Sometimes	Often
❶ let other people read your writing?	1	2	3	4
❷ read your writing aloud to listeners?	1	2	3	4
❸ use comments from people to improve your writing?	1	2	3	4
❹ mark your revisions on your draft?	1	2	3	4
❺ add important information to your draft?	1	2	3	4
❻ remove unimportant information from your draft?	1	2	3	4
❼ check that your paragraphs match your graphic organizer?	1	2	3	4
❽ make a new graphic organizer?	1	2	3	4
❾ add transition words and phrases?	1	2	3	4
❿ combine short sentences?	1	2	3	4
⓫ break up overly long sentences?	1	2	3	4
⓬ cut unnecessary words?	1	2	3	4
⓭ use a thesaurus?	1	2	3	4

Directions: Answer questions 14 and 15. If you need more room, use the back of the page.

14. To whom do you show your writing? _____

_____

15. Why do you show people your writing? _____

_____

Name _____

Date _____

Self-Assessment: Editing and Proofreading

Directions: Read the questions about what people do when editing and proofreading their compositions. Circle the numbers that show how often you do these things.

How often do you . . .	Never	Rarely	Sometimes	Often
❶ use an editing checklist?	1	2	3	4
❷ mark errors and possible errors?	1	2	3	4
❸ check in reference materials (dictionary, grammar book, style manual)?	1	2	3	4
❹ correct grammar errors?	1	2	3	4
❺ correct usage errors?	1	2	3	4
❻ correct punctuation errors?	1	2	3	4
❼ correct capitalization errors?	1	2	3	4
❽ correct spelling errors?	1	2	3	4
❾ list your most common types of errors to check for them in the future?	1	2	3	4

Directions: Answer questions 10 and 11. If you need more room, use the back of the page.

10. How many times do you usually proofread your writing before it is finished?_____

_____

11. Who do you know that is a good proofreader? Why do you think he or she is so good

at proofreading?_____

_____

Name _____

Date _____

Self-Assessment: Publishing

Directions: Read the questions about what people do when publishing their compositions. Circle the numbers that show how often you do these things.

How often do you . . .	Never	Rarely	Sometimes	Often
1 share your finished writing with people?	1	2	3	4
2 read your finished writing to people?	1	2	3	4
3 send your finished writing to be published in a book, newspaper, or magazine?	1	2	3	4
4 enter writing contests?	1	2	3	4
5 type your finished writing on a computer?	1	2	3	4
6 use different font styles or colors?	1	2	3	4
7 add pictures or graphics to your writing?	1	2	3	4
8 think about your writing after it is finished?	1	2	3	4
9 use a reflection checklist?	1	2	3	4
10 add your writing to a portfolio?	1	2	3	4

Directions: Answer questions 11 and 12. If you need more room, use the back of the page.

11. What is the last thing you do to your writing before it is finished? _____

_____

12. How do you know when your writing is finished? _____

_____

Name _____

Date _____

Prewriting Checklist

Directions: Use this checklist to help you prewrite your composition. If you do something else that helps you to get ready to write, check the last box and describe what you do.

Checklist

❑ I ask myself questions to help me think of a topic to write about.

❑ I choose my topic and save my extra ideas for other writing projects.

❑ I narrow my topic so that it is clear what I am writing about.

❑ I know who my audience is for my writing.

❑ I choose an appropriate tone for my audience.

❑ I choose a purpose and form for my writing.

❑ I use a graphic organizer to organize my ideas.

❑ I do something else that helps me to *get ready to write*. This is what I do and how it helps me:

_____

_____

_____

_____

_____

_____

_____

_____

_____

_____

_____

_____

Name _____

Date _____

Drafting Checklist

Directions: Use this checklist to help you draft your composition. If you do something else that helps you to get it down on paper, check the last box and describe what you do.

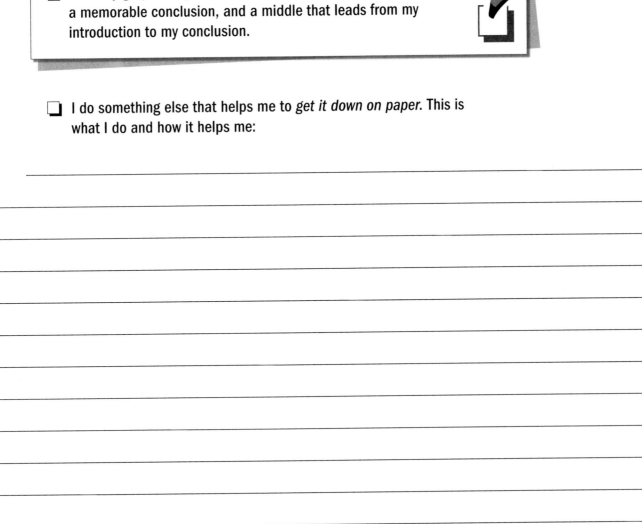

Checklist

❏ I use my prewriting ideas and information (brainstorming, FATP chart).

❏ I add information that was not included in my prewriting.

❏ I write multiple paragraphs with multiple sentences.

❏ I use my graphic organizer to create an engaging introduction, a memorable conclusion, and a middle that leads from my introduction to my conclusion.

❏ I do something else that helps me to *get it down on paper*. This is what I do and how it helps me:

_____

_____

_____

_____

_____

_____

_____

_____

_____

_____

_____

Revising Checklist

Directions: Use this checklist to help you revise your composition. If you do something else that helps you to get it to sing, check the last box and describe what you do.

Checklist

❏ I use comments from other people to revise my draft.

I check and, if necessary, revise my composition for

❏ focus and unity, deleting irrelevant or repetitive sentences;

❏ organization, referring back to my graphic organizer, reordering paragraphs, sentences, and connecting them with transitions;

❏ development of ideas, adding support such as details, facts, and quotes, to elaborate on and clarify ideas;

❏ voice and style, replacing vague words with more precise and effective words, combining and restructuring sentences for variety and effect, changing passive voice to active voice, and adjusting my tone to fit the audience.

❏ I do something else that helps me to *get it to sing*. This is what I do and how it helps me:

_____

_____

_____

_____

_____

_____

_____

_____

_____

Name _____

Date _____

Editing and Proofreading Checklist

Directions: Use this checklist to help you edit and proofread your composition. If you do something else that helps you to get it right, check the last box and describe what you do.

Checklist

❏ I use an editing checklist.

❏ I mark errors and possible errors to check.

❏ I check in reference materials (dictionary, grammar book, style manual).

When necessary, I correct my composition for errors in

❏ grammar,

❏ usage,

❏ punctuation,

❏ capitalization,

❏ spelling.

❏ I list my most common types of errors to check for them in other things that I will write.

❏ I do something else that helps me to *get it right*. This is what I do and how it helps me:

_____

_____

_____

_____

_____

_____

_____

Name _____

Date _____

Publishing Checklist

Directions: Use this checklist to help you publish your composition. If you do something else that helps you to get it out there, check the last box and describe what you do.

Checklist

❏ I create a final version of my work.

❏ I make my writing look good (by hand or on a computer).

❏ I share my writing with an audience (one person or many people).

❏ I reflect on my writing with a reflection checklist to learn about myself as a writer.

❏ I do something else that helps me to *get it out there*. This is what I do and how it helps me:

_____

_____

_____

_____

_____

_____

_____

_____

_____

_____

_____

Name _____

Date _____

Self-Assessment: Writing Traits

Directions: Complete the sentences to tell what you know about the traits of good writing.

1. When writing is focused and unified, it is _____

2. When writing is organized, a reader can _____

3. When writing is well-developed, it helps a reader _____

4. When writing has a unique voice and style, it _____

5. When writing follows written conventions, it helps you _____

Directions: Use the checklist to help you think about your writing. Which traits do you need to work on?

Checklist

1. Focus and Unity
Most of my writing is focused and unified because
- ☐ it has a clear central idea
- ☐ everything goes together

2. Organization
Most of my writing is well-organized because
- ☐ the order of my ideas are clear and go with my purpose
- ☐ my ideas flow well together
- ☐ transitions connect all my ideas

3. Development of Ideas
Most of my writing is well-developed because
- ☐ it is thoughtful and interesting
- ☐ the ideas are explained and supported

4. Voice and Style
Most of my writing is unique because
- ☐ it sounds like me
- ☐ it has colorful language
- ☐ it has varied sentences that flow together well

5. Written Conventions
Most of my writing is written correctly because
- ☐ it has few punctuation, capitalization, or spelling errors
- ☐ the meaning in each sentence is clear

Name _____

Date _____

Self-Assessment: Written Composition

Directions: Put a ✔ next to the form of writing that you used. Read your composition, and answer questions 1–4.

Writing Form

- ☐ reflective essay
- ☐ persuasive essay
- ☐ news article
- ☐ letter of problem solving
- ☐ literary critique
- ☐ poem in free verse
- ☐ short, short story
- ☐ résumé
- ☐ _____

1. What do you like best about your composition?

   _____

   _____

   _____

2. What did you do well?

   _____

   _____

   _____

3. What could you improve about your composition?

   _____

   _____

   _____

4. What will you remember to work on in your next composition?

   _____

   _____

   _____

Name _____

Date _____

Peer-Assessment: Written Composition

Directions: Put a ✔ next to the form of writing that your partner used. Read your partner's composition, and answer questions 1–4.

Writing Form

- ☐ reflective essay
- ☐ letter of problem solving
- ☐ short, short story

- ☐ persuasive essay
- ☐ literary critique
- ☐ résumé

- ☐ news article
- ☐ poem in free verse
- ☐ _____

1. What did you like best about your partner's composition?

   _____

   _____

   _____

2. What did your partner do well?

   _____

   _____

   _____

3. What could your partner improve about his or her composition?

   _____

   _____

   _____

4. What should your partner remember to do when writing the next composition?

   _____

   _____

   _____

Name _____

Date _____

Troubleshooting Checklist

Directions: Use this checklist to help you revise your composition. Write your revision on a separate sheet of paper.

☐ **My writing holds together.** If not, try these solutions:
- Speak Your Truth
- Explain Your Truth

☐ **I wrote enough.** If not, try these solutions:
- Get Into an Argument
- Prove It On Your Own
- Ba-Da-Bing!

☐ **My ideas are connected.** If not, try these solutions:
- Take Time for Transitions
- Connect Your Paragraphs

☐ **My writing is precise and full of details.** If not, try these solutions:
- Use the Intensity Scale
- Add Snapshots and Thoughtshots
- Get on Target

☐ **My writing moves along in an interesting way.** If not, try these solutions:
- Add Meat to the Bones
- Zero In on a Moment

☐ **I get to the point without extra words.** If not, try these solutions:
- Take Out Throw Away Writing
- Use Fewer Words

☐ **My sentences are interesting.** If not, try these solutions:
- Vary Your Sentences
- Spice Up Your Verbs
- Pepper Your Writing with Prepositional Phrases
- Move a Modifier
- Elaborate With Participles
- Elaborate With Clauses
- Elaborate With Absolutes

Name _____

Date _____

Self-Assessment: How Am I Doing with the Research Process?

Directions: For many people, some stages of the research process are easier to do than others. Read the list of things people do when they research. Circle the numbers that show how hard or how easy you think each stage is.

	Hard	Somewhat Hard	Somewhat Easy	Easy
1 Planning your research	1	2	3	4
2 Finding sources for information	1	2	3	4
3 Choosing which sources to use	1	2	3	4
4 Taking notes from your sources	1	2	3	4
5 Making sense of your notes	1	2	3	4
6 Turning your notes into an outline	1	2	3	4
7 Adding your research to your report	1	2	3	4
8 Citing the sources you used	1	2	3	4

Directions: Answer questions 9 and 10. If you need more room, use the back of the page.

9. Which stage of the research process do you think is the easiest? Explain why. _____

_____

_____

10. Which stage of the research process do you think is the hardest? Explain why. _____

_____

_____

Name _____

Date _____

Research Process Reflection Form

Directions: Reflect on the process you used to research your composition.
Write the title of your composition here: _____.

Gathering Information

1. What did you do that helped you gather information for your composition? _____

_____

_____

2. What will you do differently when you gather information for your next composition? _____

_____

_____

Organizing and Digesting Information

3. What did you do that helped you organize and digest information for your composition? _____

_____

_____

4. What will you do differently when you organize and digest information for your next composition?

_____

_____

Presenting Information

5. What did you do that helped you present information in your composition? _____

_____

_____

6. What will you do differently when you present information in your next composition? _____

_____

_____

Name _____

Date _____

Self-Assessment: Digging Up the Facts

Directions: Read the questions about what people do when digging up facts for their compositions. Circle the numbers that show how often you do these things.

How often do you . . .	Never	Rarely	Sometimes	Often
❶ write research questions before searching for information?	1	2	3	4
❷ narrow the focus of your research topic?	1	2	3	4
❸ plan your search before starting?	1	2	3	4
❹ use the library?	1	2	3	4
❺ research in books?	1	2	3	4
❻ research on the Internet?	1	2	3	4
❼ research by interviewing people?	1	2	3	4
❽ take notes?	1	2	3	4
❾ avoid plagiarism?	1	2	3	4

Directions: Answer questions 10–12. If you need more room, use the back of the page.

10. What topics would you like to learn more about? _____

_____

11. How do you take notes? _____

_____

12. How would you feel if someone plagiarized your writing? _____

_____

Name _____

Date _____

Self-Assessment: Making Sense of Your Notes

Directions: Read the questions about what people do when making sense of their notes for their compositions. Circle the numbers that show how often you do these things.

How often do you . . .	Never	Rarely	Sometimes	Often
❶ group your notes by related ideas?	1	2	3	4
❷ check to see if your notes answer your research questions?	1	2	3	4
❸ do more research if you do not have enough information to answer your research questions?	1	2	3	4
❹ use your notes to write an outline for your composition?	1	2	3	4

Directions: Answer questions 5 and 6. If you need more room, use the back of the page.

5. How do you keep your notes organized? _____

_____

_____

_____

_____

6. How do you decide if you have enough research information for your report? _____

_____

_____

_____

_____

Name _____

Date _____

Self-Assessment: Packaging Your Ideas

Directions: Read the questions about what people do when packaging their ideas in their compositions. Circle the numbers that show how often you do these things.

How often do you . . .	Never	Rarely	Sometimes	Often
❶ use your outline to draft your composition?	1	2	3	4
❷ add research information to your composition?	1	2	3	4
❸ revise and edit your composition?	1	2	3	4
❹ list your sources in a works cited page?	1	2	3	4
❺ add visuals to your composition?	1	2	3	4
❻ add sound to your composition?	1	2	3	4
❼ use technology to present your composition?	1	2	3	4
❽ practice presenting your composition?	1	2	3	4

Directions: Answer questions 9 and 10. If you need more room, use the back of the page.

9. How do you know when you have finished writing your report? _____

_____

10. How do you know when you are ready to present your report? _____

_____

Name _____

Date _____

Digging Up the Facts Checklist

Directions: Use this checklist to help you dig up facts for your composition. If you do something else that helps you to gather information, check the last box and describe what you do.

Checklist

❏ I write research questions before searching for information.

❏ I narrow the focus of my research topic.

❏ I plan my search.

❏ I use different sources, such as books, the Internet, magazines, and interviews.

❏ I take careful notes.

❏ I avoid plagiarism.

❏ I do something else that helps me to gather information for my composition. This is what I do and how it helps me:

_____

_____

_____

_____

_____

_____

_____

_____

_____

Making Sense of Your Notes Checklist

Directions: Use this checklist to help you make sense of your notes for your composition. If you do something else that helps you to organize and digest information, check the last box and describe what you do.

Checklist

❏ I group my notes by related ideas.

❏ I check to see if my notes answer my research questions.

❏ I do more research if I did not have enough information to answer my research questions.

❏ I use my notes to write an outline for my report.

❏ I do something else that helps me to organize and digest information for my composition. This is what I do and how it helps me:

_____

_____

_____

_____

_____

_____

_____

_____

_____

_____

Name _____

Date _____

Packaging Your Ideas Checklist

Directions: Use this checklist to help you package your ideas in your composition. If you do something else that helps you to present information, check the last box and describe what you do.

❑ I use my outline to draft my composition.

❑ I add my research information to my composition.

❑ I revise and edit my composition.

❑ I list my sources in a works-cited page.

❑ I add visuals to my composition.

❑ I add sounds to my composition.

❑ I practice presenting my composition.

❑ I do something else that helps me to present information in my composition. This is what I do and how it helps me:

_____

_____

_____

_____

_____

_____

_____

_____

_____

Answer Keys

Benchmark Tests

Expository Writing	Persuasive Writing	Literary Analysis	Narrative Writing	Reflective Writing
1. D	1. D	1. D	1. D	1. A
2. F	2. H	2. F	2. H	2. H
3. D	3. B	3. B	3. B	3. B
4. F	4. J	4. H	4. H	4. G
5. B	5. B	5. C	5. A	5. D
6. J	6. G	6. F	6. H	6. G
7. C	7. C	7. C	7. B	7. B
8. B	8. G	8. J	8. H	8. H
9. C	9. A	9. B	9. B	9. B
10. J	10. F	10. F	10. F	10. H
11. D	11. C	11. D	11. D	11. A
12. H	12. F	12. J	12. F	12. J

Conversion Chart for Benchmark Tests:

Points	1	2	3	4	5	6	7	8	9	10	11	12	13	14	15	16
%	3	6	9	13	16	19	22	25	28	31	34	38	41	44	47	50

17	18	19	20	21	22	23	24	25	26	27	28	29	30	31	32	Points
53	56	59	63	66	69	72	75	78	81	84	88	91	94	97	100	%

Chapter Tests

Chapter 1 Form A	Chapter 1 Form B	Chapter 2 Form A	Chapter 2 Form B	Chapter 5 Form A	Chapter 5 Form B
1. 5-4-2-3-1	1. 3-5-4-1-2	1. A	1. B	1. 2-4-3-1-5	1. 3-2-5-1-4
2. D	2. C	2. J	2. J	2. B	2. A
3. G	3. G	3. C	3. D	3. H	3. J
4. C	4. B	4. J	4. H	4. B	4. D
5. G	5. F	5. B	5. D	5. F	5. H
6. B	6. D	6. F	6. G	6. D	6. B
7. F	7. H	7. C	7. D	7. H	7. H
8. D	8. C	8. G	8. G	8. D	8. A
9. G	9. F	9. C	9. B	9. J	9. G
10. C	10. B	10. G	10. H	10. C	10. D